CROWN FINANCIAL MINISTRIES

Biblical Financial Study

STUDENT MANUAL

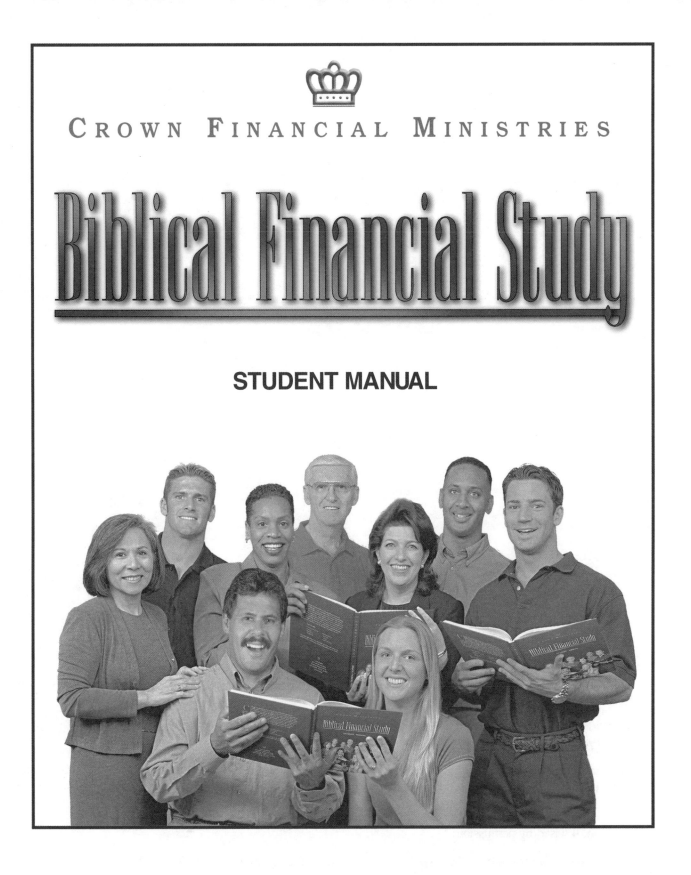

PO Box 100
Gainesville GA 30503-0100
1-800-722-1976 • www.crown.org

Interior design and typesetting by Tim Howard.

September 2000 Edition

SMALL GROUP STUDY SCHEDULE

MY SMALL GROUP STUDY

Day and time it meets: _____ Date of first meeting: _____

Where it meets: _____

My leaders are: _____ Phone: _____

_____ Phone: _____

NOTE: Any regularly scheduled class that falls on a holiday or other special event may be rescheduled.

REQUIREMENTS

Before you participate in this study you must read *Your Money Counts*. In addition, you must complete these four requirements before each weekly meeting:

1. HOMEWORK

- Everyone is required to complete the homework in writing. The homework questions are designed to take approximately 15 minutes each day to complete. Space is provided in the Student Manual to answer the homework questions. If a couple is taking the study together, they will each have a student manual.

2. SCRIPTURE MEMORY

- Everyone memorizes an assigned verse each week and then individually recites the verse at the beginning of class.

3. PRACTICAL APPLICATION

- Each week everyone completes a practical financial exercise, such as beginning a budget or formulating a debt repayment schedule.

4. PRAYER

- Everyone prays for his or her group members each day.

> If for any reason someone does not complete all the requirements for a particular week, the leader is not to allow him or her to participate in the discussion that week. This accountability cultivates faithfulness, and the more faithful a person is, the more benefits he will derive from the study.

- Moreover, everyone must attend at least ten of the twelve weekly studies. Each class lasts two hours. Should anyone miss a meeting or anticipate being late for class, please notify one of the leaders in advance. The meetings will begin and end on time.
- In addition to these requirements, we encourage everyone to teach these biblical principles to their children if they have a family.

PURPOSE

*The purpose of the CROWN study
is to teach people God's financial principles
in order to know Christ more intimately
and to be free to serve Him.*

FINANCIAL POLICY

- CROWN FINANCIAL MINISTRIES does not endorse, recommend, or sell any financial investments or services. No one may use affiliation with CROWN to promote or influence the sale of any financial products or services.
- The CROWN FINANCIAL MINISTRIES small group study does not give specific investment advice. No one may use his or her affiliation with CROWN to give investment advice.
- This study is affordably priced because we do not want cost to be an obstacle to people who desire to participate. If you find the study valuable and want to help make it available to others, you may make a tax deductible gift to CROWN FINANCIAL MINISTRIES.

WEB SITE

CROWN has designed a World Wide Web location as a resource to provide students and leaders with up-to-date and detailed financial information. It contains the forms used in this study, helpful articles, a categorized list of the verses dealing with possessions, links to other useful web sites, and much more.

Visit the web site at www.crown.org for a world of information.

INTRODUCTION
How We Handle Money Impacts Our Relationship With the Lord

THE MASTER REWARDS HIS FAITHFUL SERVANTS—
*"Well done, good and faithful servant . . .
enter into the joy of your master."*
Matthew 25:21

*"If therefore you have not been faithful in the use of worldly
wealth, who will entrust the true riches to you?"*
Luke 16:11

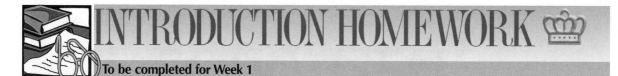
Scripture to Memorize:

> *"If therefore you have not been faithful in the use of worldly wealth*, who will entrust the true riches to you?"* (Luke 16:11).
>
> * The words *worldly wealth* from the New International Version have been substituted for the words *unrighteous mammon* from the New American Standard Version to clarify the meaning of this passage.

Before attending the first class complete the □ Scripture to Memorize, □ Practical Application and □ Homework.

 Practical Application: □ Read *Your Money Counts* prior to the first meeting.

HOMEWORK:

1. What was the most helpful information you learned from reading *Your Money Counts*?

Read *Isaiah 55:8-9*

2. Based on this passage, do you think God's financial principles will differ from how most people handle money? What do you think would be the greatest difference?

Then read Luke 16:11.

3. What does this verse communicate to you about the importance of managing possessions faithfully?

4. How does handling money impact our fellowship with the Lord?

Scripture memory helps: The memory verses are found in the back of the *Practical Application Workbook* and are designed to be removed and carried with you throughout the day. The verses have been set to music on an audio cassette which may be obtained by using the form at the end of the *Practical Application Workbook* or by visiting CROWN's web site www.crown.org

INTRODUCTION

INTRODUCTION NOTES ♔

Please do not read these notes until you completed the Introduction Homework.

Two economic systems operate in the world: God's economy and the economy that people invent. Scripture reveals God's economy to us in great detail.

The way most people handle money is in sharp contrast to God's financial principles. This should not surprise us. Isaiah 55:8 reads, *"For My thoughts are not your thoughts, neither are your ways My ways', declares the Lord."* The most significant difference between these economic systems is that in God's economy, the living Lord plays the central role. As elementary as this sounds, this distinction has profound implications.

It is difficult for some people to think of God as being involved with our finances, because God has chosen to be invisible and operates in the unseen supernatural realm.

Jesus said more about money than almost any other subject.

THE BIBLE AND MONEY

It may surprise you to learn just how much the Bible says about finances. There are more than 2,350 verses on how to handle money and possessions. Moreover, Jesus Christ said more about money than almost any other subject.

We need to ask ourselves why Christ said so much about money. He lived in a much simpler society than ours. He never had to struggle with a credit card, and He never had to reconcile a checkbook! Nevertheless, our Lord consistently addressed the issue of money for three reasons.

1. *How We Handle Our Money Influences Our Fellowship with the Lord*
Jesus equates how we handle our money with the quality of our spiritual life. In Luke 16:11, He says, *"If therefore you have not been faithful in the use of worldly wealth,˚ who will entrust the true riches to you?"* If we handle our money properly according to the principles of Scripture, our fellowship with Christ is going to grow closer. However, if we are unfaithful, our fellowship with Him will suffer.

This is illustrated in the parable of the talents. The master congratulates the servant who had managed money faithfully: *"Well done, good and faithful servant; you were faithful with a few things; I will put you in charge of many things. Enter into the joy of your master"* (Matthew 25:21). As we handle money God's way, we have an opportunity to enter into the joy of a more intimate relationship with our Lord. Sadly, this is a biblical truth most people have failed to grasp.

2. Possessions Compete with the Lord for First Place in our Lives

Money is a primary competitor with Christ for the lordship of our lives. Jesus tells us we must choose to serve only one of these two masters. *"No one can serve two masters; for either he will hate the one and love the other, or he will hold to one and despise the other. You cannot serve God and mammon* [money]*"* (Matthew 6:24). It is impossible for us to serve money—even in a small way—and still serve the Lord.

When the Crusades were being fought during the 12th Century, the Crusaders hired mercenaries to fight for them. Because it was a religious war, the mercenaries were baptized before fighting. As they were being baptized, the soldiers would take their swords and hold them out of the water to symbolize that Jesus Christ was not in control of their swords. They had the freedom to use their weapons in any way they wished.

Though they may not be as obvious about it as were the mercenaries, many people today handle their money in a similar fashion. Some Christians hold their wallet or purse "out of the water," in effect saying, "God, you may be the lord of my entire life, except in the area of money—I am perfectly capable of handling that myself."

3. Much of Life Revolves Around the Use of Money

The Lord talked so much about money because He knew that much of our lives would center around its use. During your normal week, how much time do you spend earning money in your job, making decisions on how to spend money, thinking about where to save and invest money, or praying about your giving? Fortunately, God has prepared us by giving us the Bible as His roadmap for living.

A DIVISION OF RESPONSIBILITIES

A close friend, Jim Seneff, challenged me to join him in a study of Scripture to find out what the Lord said about handling money. We read the entire Bible, identified each of the 2,350 verses, then arranged them by categories according to their various topics. Not only were we surprised at how practical the Word of God is in this area, but we discovered a division of responsibilities in the handling of our money. Simply put: God has a part, and we have a part.

God has retained certain responsibilities and has delegated other responsibilities to us. Most of the frustration we experience in handling money is because we do not realize which responsibilities are ours and which are not. However, when we learn God's responsibilities and do our part faithfully, we can experience contentment.

Contentment is mentioned seven times in the Bible, and six times it has to do with money. One of our goals during this study will be to learn to become content. In Philippians 4:11-12 Paul writes, *"For I have learned to be content in whatever circumstances I am. I know how to get along with humble means, and I also know how to live in prosperity."* Examine these verses carefully. We are not born with the instinct of contentment; rather, it is something we must learn. The second week's homework assignment will address God's Part, the foundation to contentment.

As you complete the homework for God's Part, it may seem as if God does everything. However, the Lord has given us specific responsibilities to fulfill. We will be studying our various responsibilities for ten full weeks.

Contentment is mentioned seven times in the Bible, and six times it has to do with money.

GOD'S PART

Lord Is Owner of All

DAVID—
WORSHIPING THE LORD AT THE DEDICATION OF THE
OFFERING FOR THE TEMPLE

"Everything in the heavens and earth is yours, O Lord . . ."
1 Chronicles 29:11, LB

GOD'S PART HOMEWORK

To Be Completed for Week 2

 Scripture to Memorize:

"Everything in the heavens and earth is yours, O Lord, and this is your king-dom. We adore you as being in control of everything. Riches and honor come from you alone, and you are the Ruler of all mankind; your hand controls power and might and it is at your discretion that men are made great and given strength" (1 Chronicles 29:11-12, LB).

Practical Application:

☐ Complete the Personal Financial Statement.   ☐ Begin keeping a record of everything you spend.
☐ Make an appointment with an attorney to prepare a current will if you do not have one.

DAY ONE

1. Read the Introduction Notes on pages 9 to 11 and answer: What information especially interested you?

2. Comment on any personal challenges you felt after learning the three reasons the Bible says so much about money.

DAY TWO

Read *Deuteronomy 10:14; Psalm 24:1;* and *1 Corinthians 10:26.*

1. What do these passages teach about the ownership of your possessions?

GOD'S PART

Then read *Leviticus 25:23; Psalm 50:10-12; and Haggai 2:8.*

2. What are some of the specific items that the Lord owns?

    Leviticus 25:23—

    Psalm 50:10-12—

    Haggai 2:8—

3. Prayerfully evaluate your attitude of ownership toward your possessions. Do you consistently recognize the true owner of those possessions? Give two practical suggestions to help recognize God's ownership.

    ■

    ■

DAY THREE

Read *1 Chronicles 29:11-12 and Psalm 135:6.*

1. What do these verses say about the Lord's control of circumstances?

Then read *Proverbs 21:1; Isaiah 40:21-24;* **and** *Acts 17:26.*

2. What do these passages tell you about the Lord's control of people?

   Proverbs 21:1—

   Isaiah 40:21-24—

   Acts 17:26—

3. Do you normally recognize the Lord's control of all events? If not, how can you become more consistent in recognizing His control?

DAY FOUR

Read *Genesis 45:4-8; Genesis 50:19-20;* **and** *Romans 8:28.*

1. Why is it important to realize that God controls and uses even difficult circumstances for good in the life a godly person?

2. How does this perspective impact you today?

3. Share a difficult circumstance you have experienced and how the Lord ultimately used it for good in your life.

DAY FIVE

Read *Psalm 34:9-10; Matthew 6:31-33;* **and** *Philippians 4:19.*

1. What has the Lord promised about meeting your needs?

2. Give an example from the Bible of the Lord providing for someone's needs in a supernatural way.

3. How does this apply to you today?

DAY SIX

Read *Job 1:20-22* and *Jeremiah 27:5*.

1. What do these verses communicate to you about how the Lord distributes material possessions?

Job 1:20-22—

Jeremiah 27:5—

Then read *Matthew 25:14-15*.

2. What does this passage tell us about how the Lord dispenses material possessions?

3. How should this influence our perspective of those who have more or less than we do?

 Please write your prayer requests in your prayer log before coming to class.

I will take the following action as a result of this week's study:

GOD'S PART NOTES

Please do not read these notes until you completed the God's Part Homework.

In Scripture God calls Himself by more than 250 names. The name that best describes God's part in the area of money is Master. This is the most important section of the entire study, because how we view God determines how we live.

After losing his children and all his possessions, Job was able to worship God because he knew the Lord and the Lord's role as Master of those possessions. Why did Moses forsake the treasures of Egypt and choose to suffer with the people of God? It was because Moses knew the Lord and accepted His role as Master. There are four parts to God's position as Master.

GOD'S PART

OWNERSHIP

The Lord owns all our possessions. *"Behold, to the Lord your God belong . . . the earth and all that is in it"* (Deuteronomy 10:14). *"The earth is the Lord's, and all it contains"* (Psalm 24:1).

Scripture even reveals specific items God owns. Leviticus 25:23 identifies Him as the owner of all the land: *"The land, moreover, shall not be sold permanently, for the land* is Mine." Haggai 2:8 says that He owns the precious metals: *"'The silver is Mine,* and *the gold is Mine,' declares the Lord of hosts."* And in Psalm 50:10-12, the Scriptures tell us: *"For every beast of the forest is Mine, the cattle on a thousand hills . . . everything that moves in the field is Mine. If I were hungry, I would not tell you; for the world is Mine, and all it contains."*

The Lord created all things, and He never transferred the ownership of His creation to people. In Colossians 1:17 we are told that, *"In Him all things hold together."* At this very moment the Lord holds everything together by His power. As we will see throughout this study, recognizing God's ownership is crucial in allowing Jesus Christ to become the Lord of our money and possessions.

When we acknowledge God's ownership, every spending decision becomes a spiritual decision.

Ownership or Lordship?

If we are going to be genuine followers of Christ, we must transfer ownership of our possessions to the Lord. *"So therefore, no one of you can be My disciple who does not give up all his own possessions"* (Luke 14:33). We must give up all claim to ownership of all that we have. I have found that the Lord will sometimes test us by asking that we be willing to give up the very possession that is most important to us.

The most vivid example of this in Scripture is when the Lord instructed Abraham to *"take now your son, your only son, whom you love, Isaac . . . and offer him there as a burnt offering"* (Genesis 22:2). When Abraham obeyed, demonstrating his willingness to give up his dearest possession, God responded, *"Do not stretch out your hand against the lad . . . for now I know that you fear God, since you have not withheld your son, your only son, from Me"* (Genesis 22:12).

When we acknowledge God's ownership, every spending decision becomes a spiritual decision. No longer do we ask, "Lord, what do You want me to do with **my** money?" It becomes, "Lord, what do You want me to do with **Your** money?" When we have this perspective and prayerfully handle His money according to His wishes, spending and saving decisions become as spiritual as giving decisions.

Where did God get all the financing for this!?

The Lord's ownership also influences how we care for possessions. For example, because the Lord is the owner of where we live, we want to please Him by keeping His home cleaner and in better repair!

Contentment

Recognizing the Lord's ownership is important in learning contentment. If you believe that you own a particular possession, then the circumstances surrounding that possession will affect your attitude. If it's a favorable situation, you will be happy. If it's an adverse circumstance, you will be discontent.

Shortly after Jim came to grips with God's ownership, he purchased a new car. He had driven the car only two days before someone rammed into the side of it. Jim's first reaction was "Lord, I don't know why You want a dent in Your car, but now You've got a big one!" Jim was learning contentment!

Recognizing God's Ownership

Consistently recognizing God's ownership is difficult. It is easy to believe intellectually that God owns all you have, but still live as if this were not true. Our culture suggests an opposing view. Everything around us—the media, even the law—say, that what you possess, you, and you alone, own. Genuinely acknowledging God's ownership requires nothing less than a total change of perception.

Here are a number of practical suggestions to help us recognize God's ownership:

- For the next 30 days meditate on 1 Chronicles 29:11-12 when you first awake and just before going to sleep.
- Be careful in the use of personal pronouns; consider substituting "the" or "the Lord's" for "my," "mine," and "ours."
- Ask the Lord to make you aware of His ownership and make you willing to relinquish ownership. Make this a special object of prayer during the next 30 days.
- Establish the habit of acknowledging the Lord's ownership every time you purchase an item.

CONTROL

Besides being Creator and Owner, God is ultimately in control of every event that occurs upon the earth. *"We adore you as being in control of everything"* (1 Chronicles 29:11, LB). *"Whatever the Lord pleases He does, in heaven and in earth"* (Psalm 135:6). And in the book of Daniel, King Nebuchadnezzar stated: *"I praised the Most High; I honored and glorified Him who lives forever . . . All the peoples of the earth are regarded as nothing. He does as He pleases with the powers of heaven and the peoples of the earth. No one can hold back His hand or say to Him: 'What have you done?'"* (Daniel 4:34-35).

The Lord is in control even of difficult events. *"I am the Lord, and there is no other, the One forming light and creating darkness, causing well-being and creating calamity; I am the Lord who does all these"* (Isaiah 45:6-7).

It is important for the child of God to realize that His heavenly Father uses even seemingly devastating circumstances for ultimate good in the lives of the godly. *"And we know that God causes all things to work together for good for those who love God, to those who are called according to His purpose"* (Romans 8:28). The Lord allows difficult circumstances for three reasons:

1. He Accomplishes His Intentions

This illustrated in the life of Joseph who, as a teenager, was sold into slavery by his jealous brothers. Joseph comprehended this and responded correctly to his brothers: *"Do not be grieved or angry with yourselves, because you sold me here for God sent me before you to preserve life . . . it was not you who sent me here, but God . . . And as for you, you meant evil against me, but God meant it for good in order to bring about this present result, to preserve many people alive"* (Genesis 45:5-8; 50:20).

2. He Develops Our Character

Godly character, something that is precious in the sight of the Lord, often is developed during trying times. Romans 5:3-4 reads, *"We also exult in our tribulations, knowing that tribulation brings about perseverance; and perseverance, proven character."*

3. He Disciplines His Children

"For those whom the Lord loves He disciplines . . . He disciplines us for our good, that we may share His holiness. All discipline for the moment seems not to be joyful but sorrowful; yet to those who have been trained by it, afterwards it yields the peaceful fruit of righteousness" (Hebrews 12:6, 10-11). When we are disobedient, we can expect our loving Lord to administer discipline, often through difficult circumstances, to encourage us to abandon our sin and "share His holiness."

You can be content knowing that your loving heavenly Father is in control of every situation that you will ever face, and He intends to use every one for a good purpose.

GOD IS THE PROVIDER

The Lord promises to provide our needs. *"But seek ye first the kingdom of God and His righteousness, and all these things* [food and clothing] *shall be added unto you"* (Matthew 6:33, KJV).

The same Lord who fed manna to the children of Israel during their 40 years of wandering in the wilderness and who fed 5,000 with only five loaves and two fish has promised to provide our needs. This is the same Lord who told Elijah, *"I have commanded the ravens to provide for you . . . and the ravens brought him bread and meat in the morning and bread and meat in the evening"* (1 Kings 17:4,6).

God is both predictable and unpredictable. He is absolutely predictable in His faithfulness to provide for our needs. What we cannot predict is how the Lord will provide. He uses various and often surprising means of meeting our needs—an increase in income or a gift. He may provide an opportunity to stretch our limited resources through money-saving purchases. Regardless of how He chooses to provide for our needs, He is completely reliable.

Elijah

The Lord instructs us to be content when our basic needs are met. *"And if we have food and covering, with these we shall be content"* (1 Timothy 6:8). Charles Allen tells a story illustrating this principle: As World War II was drawing to a close, the Allied armies gathered up many orphans and placed them in camps where they were well fed. Despite excellent care, they were afraid and slept poorly.

Finally, a psychologist came up with a solution. Each child was given a piece of bread to hold after he was put to bed. If he was hungry, more food was provided, but when he was finished, this particular piece of bread was just to be held—not eaten. The piece of bread produced wonderful results. The children went to bed knowing that they would have food to eat the next day. That guarantee gave the children a restful and contented sleep.

Similarly, the Lord has given us His guarantee—our "piece of bread." As we cling to His promises of provision, we can relax and be content. *"And my God shall supply all your needs according to His riches"* (Philippians 4:19).

Needs vs. Wants

It is important to understand the distinction between a need and a want. The definition of a need is one of the **basic necessities of life**, which are food, clothing and shelter. A want is **anything in excess of a need**. The Lord may allow us to have our wants fulfilled, but He has not promised to provide every want.

GOD GIVES US OUR POSSESSIONS

The Lord sovereignly dispenses possessions to whomever and in what quantity He chooses. *"Both riches and honor come from You . . . all things come from You"* (1 Chronicles 29:12-14). Our heavenly Father does not give possessions equally to all His children. This is demonstrated in the parable of the talents: *"And to one he gave five talents, to another, two, and to another, one, each according to his own ability"* (Matthew 25:15).

Not only does the Lord give material possessions, but He also sometimes allows them to be taken away. Job 1:20-21 reads, *"Then Job arose and tore his robe and shaved his head, and he fell to the ground and worshiped. And he said, 'Naked I came from my mother's womb, and naked I shall return there. The Lord gave, and the Lord has taken away. Blessed be the name of the Lord.'"*

God, as He is revealed in Scripture, is much different than the way people commonly imagine Him to be. Our tendency is to shrink God down and fit Him into a mold with human abilities and limitations. Our failure to recognize God's Part is due to the fact we do not understand the greatness of God, *"who stretched out the heavens and laid the foundations of the earth"* (Isaiah 51:13). We expand our vision to capture the true perspective of God primarily through studying what the Bible tells us about Him. The following are only a few:

He is Lord of the Universe

Carefully review some of His names and attributes: Creator, the Almighty, eternal, all-knowing, all-powerful, omnipresent, awesome, Lord of lords and King of kings.

The Lord's power and ability are beyond our understanding. Astronomers estimate that there are more than 100 billion galaxies in the universe, each containing billions of stars. The distance from one end of a galaxy to the other is often measured in millions of light years. Though our sun is a relatively small star, it could contain more than one million earths, and it has temperatures of 20 million degrees at its center. Isaiah 40:25 reads, *"Lift up your eyes on high and see who has created these stars, the One who leads forth their host be number, He calls them all by name; because of the greatness of His might and the strength of His power not one of them is missing."*

He is Lord of the Nations

Examine the Lord's role and position relative to nations and people. Isaiah 40:21-24 tells us, *"Do you not know? Have you not heard? . . . It is He who sits above the vault of the earth, and its inhabitants are like grasshoppers . . . He it is who reduces rules to nothing, who makes the judges of the earth meaningless. Scarcely have they been planted, scarcely have they been sown, scarcely has their stock taken root in the earth, but He merely blows on them, and they wither."*

From Isaiah 40:15, 17 we read, *"Behold, the nations are like a drop from a bucket, and are regarded as a speck of dust on the scales . . . all the nations are as nothing before Him, they are regarded by Him as less than nothing and meaningless."*

God doesn't fret over nations and their leaders as if He had no power to intervene. Acts 17:26 says, *"He [the Lord] . . . scattered the nations across the face of the earth. He decided beforehand which should rise and fall, and when. He determined their boundaries"* (LB).

God, as He is revealed in Scripture, is much different than the way people commonly imagine Him to be.

GOD'S PART NOTES

He is Lord of the Individual

God is intimately involved with each of us as individuals. Psalm 139:3-4, 16 reveals, *"You are familiar with all my ways. Before a word is on my tongue You know it completely, O Lord . . . All the days ordained for me were written in your book before one of them came to be"* (NIV). The Lord is so involved in our lives that He reassures us, *"The very hairs of your head are numbered"* (Matthew 10:30). Our heavenly Father is the One who knows us the best and loves us the most.

God hung the stars in space, fashioned the earth's towering mountains and mighty oceans and determined the destiny of nations. Jeremiah observed correctly: *"Nothing is too difficult for You"* (Jeremiah 32:17). Yet God knows when a sparrow falls to the ground. Nothing in this study is more important than "catching the vision" of who God is and what His part is in our finances.

SUMMARY

The Lord did not design people to carry the yoke of the responsibilities only He is capable of shouldering. Jesus said, *"Come unto Me, all who are weary and heavy-laden, and I will give you rest. Take My yoke upon you . . . For My yoke is easy, and My load light"* (Matthew 11:28-30). God has assumed the burdens of ownership, control, and provision and distribution of possessions. For this reason, His yoke is easy, and we can rest.

When I first studied God's Part, there was nothing that particularly surprised me. I vaguely knew all these truths. My problem is that I do not always live as if they are true. Our culture contributes to this problem. God is thought to play no part in financial matters, and we have, in some measure, been influenced by that view. Another reason for this difficulty is that God has chosen to be invisible. Anything that is "out of sight" tends to become "out of mind." I get out of the habit of consistently recognizing His ownership, control, and provision.

After learning God's Part, some think that little responsibility remains for us. As we begin studying Our Part in the next lesson, we will discover the Lord has given us great responsibility.

OUR PART
Faithfulness Required

ABRAHAM — FAITHFUL EVEN WITH SMALL THINGS
"Abram said to the king of Sodom, I have sworn to the Lord. . . . that I will not take a thread or a sandal thong or anything that is yours."

Genesis 14:22-23

Moreover, it is required in stewards
that a man be found faithful."
1 Corinthians 4:2, KJV

Scripture to Memorize:

"Moreover, it is required in stewards that a man be found faithful"
(1 Corinthians 4:2, KJV).

Practical Application: ☐ Complete the Deed and bring it with you to your group. The members of your group will witness your deed to help hold you accountable in the recognition of God's ownership. ☐ Also, complete the Financial Goals practical application.

DAY ONE

Read the God's Part Notes on pages 18 to 23 and answer:

1. Do you encounter difficulty in consistently recognizing the Lord's ownership of all you possess? If so, what contributes to this difficulty?

2. How can you work to be more consistent in recognizing His ownership?

3. What personal benefits do you anticipate from this consistency?

Read *Genesis 1:26* and *Psalm 8:4-6.*

1. What do these verses say about the authority God gave people?

Then read *1 Corinthians 4:2.*

2. According to this verse what is your requirement as a steward?

3. How would you define a steward?

Read *Hebrews 4:13* and *Psalm 139:1-3* **and answer:**

1. Is the Lord aware of all your thoughts and actions?

Then read *Romans 14:10-12,* **and answer.**

2. What will happen to each of us in the future?

3. How should this impact the way you live and spend money?

Read the parable of the talents in *Matthew 25:14-30.*

What does the parable illustrate about:

1. Our authority as stewards *(Matthew 25:14)*?

2. Our responsibilities?

3. Differing material resources given to each of us *(Matthew 25:15)*?

4. Our being accountable for our actions *(Matthew 25:19)*?

5. What blessings did the master give to the faithful stewards *(Matthew 25:20-23)*?

6. Other principles?

Read *Luke 16:1-2.*

1. Why did the master remove the steward from his position?

2. How do you think this principle is applicable today?

Then read *Luke 16:10.*

3. Describe the principle found in this verse.

4. How does this apply in your situation?

Then read *Luke 16:12.*

5. Are we required to be faithful with other people's possessions? What happens if we are not?

6. How does this apply to you?

 Please write your prayer requests in your prayer log before coming to class.

 I will take the following action as a result of this week's study:

OUR PART NOTES

Please do not read these notes until you completed the Our Part Homework.

The word that best describes our part is steward. The Greek word for steward is *oikonomos* which can be translated into the English word "manager". In the Bible the position of steward is one of great responsibility and has full responsibility for all his master's possessions.

As we examine Scripture we see that God, as Master, has given us the authority to be stewards. *"You made him ruler over the works of your [the Lord] hands; you put everything under his feet"* (Psalm 8:6, NIV).

> *As we examine Scripture we see that God, as Master, has given us the authority to be stewards.*

OUR RESPONSIBILITY

Our only responsibility is summed up in this verse: *"Moreover, it is required in stewards that a man be found faithful"* (1 Corinthians 4:2, KJV). Before we can be faithful, we must know what we are required to do. Just as the purchaser of complicated piece of machinery studies the manufacturer's manual to learn how to operate it, we need to examine the Creator's handbook—the Bible—to determine how He wants us to handle His possessions.

Two elements of our responsibility to be faithful are important to understand:

1. Be Faithful with What We Are Given

The Lord requires us to be faithful regardless of how much He has entrusted to us. The parable of the talents illustrates this. *"For it is just like a man about to go on a journey, who called his own servants, and entrusted his possessions to them. And to one he gave five talents, to another, two, and to another, one, each according to his own ability"* (Matthew 25:14-15).

When the owner returned, he held each servant accountable for faithfully managing his possessions. The owner commended the faithful servant who received the five talents: *"Well done, good and faithful servant; you were faithful with a few things, I will put you in charge of many things, enter into the joy of your master"* (Matthew 25:21). Interestingly, the servant who had been given two talents received the identical reward as the one who had been given the five talents (see Matthew 25:23). The Lord rewards faithfulness, regardless of the amount over which we are responsible.

We are required to be faithful whether we are given much or little. As someone once said, "It's not what I would do if $1 million were my lot; it's what I am doing with the ten dollars I've got."

2. Be Faithful in Every Area

God requires us to be faithful in handling 100 percent of our money, not just 10 percent. Unfortuately, most Christians have been taught only how to handle 10 percent of their income—the area of giving. And although this area is crucial, most have learned how to handle the other 90 percent from the world's perspective.

Study this diagram:

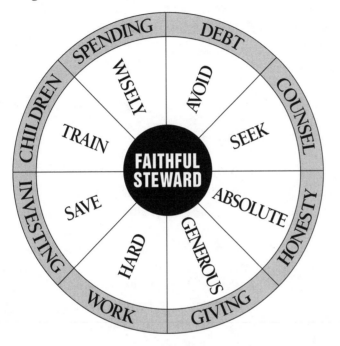

As a result of not being equipped to handle money biblically, many Christians have wrong attitudes toward possessions. This causes them to make incorrect financial decisions and to suffer painful consequences. Hosea 4:6 reads, *"My people are destroyed for lack of knowledge."*

LOVING ACCOUNTABILITY

The Lord knows **everything** about you. Hebrews 4:13 reads, *"And there is no creature hidden from His sight, but all things are open and laid bare to the eyes of Him with whom we have to do."* And from Psalm 139:1-3, *"O Lord, you have searched me and you know me. You know when I sit and when I rise; you perceive my thoughts from afar . . . you are familiar with all my ways"* (NIV).

There is nothing you will ever do or think that the Lord does not know. Your life—past, present and future—is an open book to Him. Think about that for a moment!

The thought of being fully known would be overwhelming if it were not balanced with the knowledge that the Lord also loves us deeply. My wife, Bev, created a beautiful needlepoint picture that is framed on my wall and reads, "The One who knows you best loves you most." The Lord knows you and loves you.

Just as the parable of the talents illustrates, the Lord will hold us accountable for how we handle our money: *"Now after a long time the master of those*

God requires us to be faithful in handling 100 percent of our money, not just 10 percent.

servants came and settled accounts with them" (Matthew 25:19). Second Corinthians 5:9-10 reads, *"Therefore also we have as our ambition . . . to be pleasing to Him. For we must all appear before the judgmentseat of Christ, that each one may be recompensed for his deeds in the body, according to what he has done, whether good or bad."* Each one of us will ultimately stand before the Lord and be asked to account for how we managed our money and possessions.

This perspective should motivate us to handle money strictly according to the principles of Scripture. Remember, every spending decision is a spiritual decision with eternal consequences. Our life on earth is so brief when compared with eternity; yet how we live on earth will influence how we live throughout eternity.

BENEFITS OF HANDLING MONEY FAITHFULLY

The faithful steward enjoys three benefits:

1. More Intimate Fellowship with Jesus Christ
Remember what the master said to the slave who had been faithful in discharging his financial responsibilities: *"Enter into the joy of your master"* (Matthew 25:21). We have the opportunity to enter into closer, more intimate fellowship with our Lord as we are faithful with the possessions He has given us.

Someone once told me that the Lord often allows a person to teach a particular subject because the teacher desperately needs it! That is true for me in the area of money. I have never met anyone who had more wrong attitudes about money or who handled money in a way more contrary to Scripture than did I. When I began to apply these principles, I experienced a dramatic improvement in my fellowship with the Lord. Each of these principles is intended to draw us closer to Christ.

2. The Development of Character
God uses money to refine our character. As David McConaugh explained in his book, *Money the Acid Test*, "Money, most common of temporal things, involves uncommon and eternal consequences. Even though it may be done quite unconsciously, money molds people in the process of getting it, saving it, spending it, and giving it. Depending on how it's used, it proves to be a blessing or a curse. Either the person becomes master of the money, or the money becomes the master of the person. Our Lord uses money to test our lives and as an instrument to mold us into the likeness of Himself."

All through Scripture there is an intimate correlation between the development of a person's character and how he handles money. It is regarded as an index to a person's true character. You have heard the expression, "Money talks," and indeed it does. You can tell a lot about a person's character by examining his checkbook, because we spend our money on the things that are most important to us.

We have the opportunity to enter into closer, more intimate fellowship with our Lord as we are faithful with the possessions He has given us.

3. Having Our Finances in Order

As we apply the principles of God's economy to our finances, we will begin to get out of debt, spend more wisely, start saving for our future goals, and give even more to the work of Christ.

PRINCIPLES OF FAITHFULNESS

1. If We Waste Possessions, the Lord Will Remove Us as Stewards.

"There was a certain rich man who had a steward, and this steward was reported to him as squandering his possessions. And he called him and said to him, 'What is this I hear about you? Give an account of your stewardship, for you can no longer be steward'" (Luke 16:1-2). There are two principles from this passage that are applicable to us. First of all, when we waste our possessions it becomes public knowledge and creates a poor testimony. *". . . This steward was reported to him as squandering his possessions."* Secondly, the Lord may remove us as steward if we squander what He has given us.

A local businessman earned a fortune in just three years and then went on a spending spree. Two years later he informed his office staff that he had little left and everyone would need to economize. Shortly thereafter, he left for an expensive vacation and had his office completely renovated at a cost of thousands of dollars.

I visited his office during his vacation and the entire staff was in the newly decorated office laughing over his unbridled spending habits. I left with the distinct impression the Lord would soon remove this man from the privilege of stewardship over much. And today he is on the verge of bankruptcy.

This principle is applicable today. If you waste the possessions entrusted to you, you may not be given more.

2. Faithfulness in Little Things

"He who is faithful in a very little thing is faithful also in much; and he who is unrighteous in a very little thing is unrighteous also in much" (Luke 16:10).

How do you know if a child is going to take good care of his first car? Observe how he cared for his bicycle. How do you know if a salesperson will do a competent job of serving a large client? Evaluate how he served a small client. If we have the character to be faithful with small things, the Lord knows He can trust us with greater responsibilities. Hudson Taylor said, "Small things are small things, but faithfulness with a small thing is a big thing."

3. Faithfulness with Another's Possessions

Faithfulness with another's possession will, in some measure, determine how much you are given. *"And if you have not been faithful in the use of that which is another's, who will give you that which is your own?"* (Luke 16:12).

This is a principle that is often overlooked. One of the most faithful men I know rented a vehicle from a friend. While driving the vehicle, he was involved in an accident. After explaining the situation to the owner, he took the vehicle to the owner's mechanic and instructed him, "I want you to completely restore this vehicle. Make it better than it was before the accident, and I will be responsible for the bill." What an example!

Are you faithful with other's possessions? Are you careless with your employer's office supplies? Do you waste electricity when you are staying in a motel room? When someone allows you to use something, are you careful to return it in good shape? I am certain some people have not been entrusted with more because they have been unfaithful with the possessions of others.

Please prayerfully review these principles of faithfulness.

DEBT

Debt is Slavery

A GODLY WOMAN FINDS HERSELF IN DEBT
*"My husband is dead . . . and the creditor has come
to take my two children to be his slaves. . . . "*

2 Kings 4:1

"The borrower is servant to the lender."
Proverbs 22:7, NIV

DEBT HOMEWORK

Scripture to Memorize:

"Just as the rich rule the poor, so the borrower is servant to the lender" (Proverbs 22:7, LB).

Practical Application: ☐ Complete the Debt List and the ☐ Debt Repayment Schedule for each creditor.

DAY ONE

Read the Our Part Notes on pages 30 to 34 and answer:

1. How have you observed the Lord using money to mold your character?

2. What strengths have been developed in your character?

3. What weaknesses in your character still need to be addressed?

DAY TWO

Read *Deuteronomy 15:4-6; Deuteronomy 28:1,2,12;* **and** *Deuteronomy 28:15,43-45.*

1. According to these passages how was debt viewed in the Old Testament?

2. What was the cause of someone getting in debt (becoming a borrower) or getting out of debt (becoming a lender)?

Read *Romans 13:8; Proverbs 22:7;* and *1 Corinthians 7:23* and answer:

1. Is debt encouraged in Scripture? Why?

   Romans 13:8 —

   Proverbs 22:7 —

   1 Corinthians 7:23 —

2. How does this apply to you personally and to your business?

3. Do you have a strategy to get out of debt? If you have a plan, please describe it.

DAY FOUR

Read *Psalm 37:21* and *Proverbs 3:27-28*.

1. What do these verses say about debt repayment?

   Psalm 37:21—

   Proverbs 3:27-28—

2. How will you implement this?

Read *2 Kings 4:1-7*.

1. What principles of getting out of debt can you identify from this passage?

2. Can you apply any of these principles to your present situation? How?

DAY SIX

Read *Proverbs 22:26-27* and *Proverbs 17:18* and answer:

1. What does the Bible say about cosigning (striking hands, surety)?

Proverbs 22:26-27—

Proverbs 17:18—

Then read *Proverbs 6:1-5*.

2. If someone has cosigned, what should he or she attempt to do?

 Please write your prayer requests in your prayer log before coming to class.

 I will take the following action as a result of this week's study:

"TILL DEBT DO US PART"

The amount of debt in our nation, has exploded in every area. If you converted the federal debt to one-dollar bills, placed them end-to-end and pointed them out to space, they would extend 450 million miles—beyond the sun! Corporations now owe over $4.3 trillion. Moreover, the *Wall Street Journal* reported that 51 percent of all corporate profits are being eaten up by interest.

Individuals owe more than $6.3 trillion. The average family spends $400 more than it earns each year. Personal consumer debt increases at the rate of $1,000 a second, and 13 percent of an average person's take-home pay is already committed to payment of existing debt—not including the home mortgage!

We have so much personal debt in our country that the average person has been described as someone driving on a bond-financed highway, in a bank-financed car, fueled by charge card-financed gasoline, going to purchase furniture on an installment plan to put in his savings-and-loan-financed home!

We are drowning in a sea of debt. And, with all this credit floating around, we have serious financial casualties. In a recent year more than a record 1,300,000 individuals filed bankruptcy in our country—more bankruptcies than during the Great Depression. And most sobering, a Gallup Poll found that 56 percent of all divorces are a result of financial tension in the home.

Such financial tension is created largely by believing the "Gospel According to Madison Avenue"—buy now and pay later with easy monthly payments. We all know nothing about those monthly payments is easy. Advertisers fail to tell us the whole truth. They leave out one little word . . . *debt*.

WHAT IS DEBT?

The dictionary defines debt as: "Money or property which one person is obligated to pay to another." Debt includes money owed to credit card companies, bank loans, money borrowed from relatives, the home mortgage, and past due medical bills. Bills that come due, such as the monthly electrical bill, are not considered debt if they are paid on time.

We need to understand the real cost of debt. Debt imposes both a financial and physical cost.

Credit-Card Debt

Assume you have $5,560 in credit-card debt at an 18 percent interest rate and there are no tax consequences on the interest earned or spent. This would cost you $1,000 in interest annually. Study the chart below:

1. Amount of interest you paid:

Year 5	Year 10	Year 20	Year 30	Year 40
$5,000	$10,000	$20,000	$30,000	$40,000

2. What you would accumulate on $1,000 invested annually earning 12 percent:

Year 5	Year 10	Year 20	Year 30	Year 40
6,353	17,549	72,052	241,333	767,091

3. How much the lender earns from your interest payment at 18 percent interest:

Year 5	Year 10	Year 20	Year 30	Year 40
7,154	23,521	146,628	790,948	4,163,213

You can see what lenders have known for a long time—the incredible impact of compounding interest working for you. The lender will accumulate a total of $4,163,213 if you pay him $1,000 a year for 40 years, and he earns 18 percent on your payment! Is there any wonder credit-card companies are eager for you to become one of their borrowers?

Now compare the $40,000 you paid in interest over 40 years with the $767,091 you could have accumulated, earning 12 percent on $1,000 each year. The monthly income on $767,091 is $7,671 if it's earning 12 percent—without ever touching the principal.

Stop to consider this: When a person assumes debt of $5,560 and pays $1,000 a year in interest, if he can earn a 12 percent return on an investment, he actually costs himself $767,091 over forty years. Debt has a much higher cost than many realize. Next time you are tempted to purchase something with debt, ask yourself if the long-term benefits of staying out of debt outweigh the short-term benefits of the purchase.

Home Mortgage

A 30-year home mortgage, at a 10 percent interest rate, will require you to pay more than **three times** the amount originally borrowed.

Original mortgage amount	$100,000.00
Monthly mortgage payment at 10 percent interest	$877.57
Months paid	x 360
Total payments	**$315,925.20**

The Physical Cost of Debt

Debt also often increases stress, which contributes to mental, physical, and emotional fatigue. It can stifle creativity and harm relationships. Many people raise their lifestyle through debt, only to discover that the burden of debt then controls their lifestyle. The car bumper sticker that reads, "I owe, I owe, it's off to work I go," is an unfortunate reality for too many people.

"I see your problem. You've got your creditors on your back."

WHAT SCRIPTURE SAYS ABOUT DEBT

Scripture discourages the use of debt. Read the first portion of Romans 13:8 carefully from several different Bible translations: *"Owe no man any thing"* (KJV). *"Let no debt remain outstanding"* (NIV). *"Pay all your debts"* (LB). *"Owe nothing to anyone"* (NAS). *"Keep out of debt and owe no man anything"* (Amplified).

1. Debt Is Considered Slavery

In Proverbs 22:7 we learn why our Lord speaks so directly to the area of debt: *"Just as the rich rule the poor; so the borrower is servant to the lender"* (LB). When we are in debt we are in a position of servitude to the lender. And the deeper we are in debt, the more of a servant we become. We do not have the freedom to decide where to spend our income, because our money is already legally obligated to meet these debts.

In 1 Corinthians 7:23 Paul writes, *"You were bought with a price; do not become slaves of men."* Our Father made the ultimate sacrifice by giving His Son, the Lord Jesus Christ, to die for us. And He now wants His children free to serve Him, and not our lenders, in whatever way He chooses.

2. Debt Was Considered a Curse

In the Old Testament being out of debt was one of the promised rewards for obedience. *"Now it shall be, if you will diligently obey the Lord your God, being careful to do all His commandments which I command you today, the Lord your God will set you high above all the nations of the earth. And all these blessings shall come upon you and overtake you, if you will obey the Lord your God . . . and you shall lend to many nations, but you shall not borrow"* (Deuteronomy 28:1, 2, 12).

However, indebtedness was one of the curses inflicted for disobedience. *"But it shall come about, if you will not obey the Lord your God, to observe to do all His commandments and His statutes which I charge you today, that all these curses shall come upon you and overtake you . . . The alien who is among you shall rise above you higher and higher, but you shall go down lower and lower. He shall lend to you, but you shall not lend to him; he shall be the head, and you shall be the tail"* (Deuteronomy 28:15, 43, 44).

3. Debt Presumes Upon Tomorrow

When we get into debt, we assume that we will earn enough in the future to pay the debt. We plan for our job to continue or our business or investments to be profitable. Scripture cautions us against presumption: *"Come now, you who say, 'Today or tomorrow, we shall go to such and such a city, and spend a year there and engage in business and make a profit.' Yet you do not know what your life will be like tomorrow. You are just a vapor that appears for a little while and then vanishes away. Instead, you ought to say, 'If the Lord wills, we shall live and also do this or that'"* (James 4:13-15).

4. Debt May Deny God an Opportunity

Ron Blue, an outstanding financial author, tells of a young man who wanted to go to seminary to become a missionary. The young man had no money and thought the only way he could afford seminary was to secure a student loan. However, this would have encumbered him with $40,000 of debt by the time he graduated, which would have been impossible to pay back on a missionary's salary.

After a great deal of prayer, he decided to enroll without the help of a student loan and to trust the Lord to meet his needs. He was graduated without borrowing anything and grew in his appreciation for how God could creatively provide his needs. This was the most valuable lesson learned in seminary as he prepared for life on the mission field. Borrowing may deny God an opportunity to demonstrate His reality.

BORROWING

Scripture is silent on the subject of when we can owe money. In our opinion it is possible to owe money for a home mortgage or for your business or vocation. This is permissible, we believe, only if the following three criteria are met:

- The item purchased is an asset with the potential to appreciate or produce an income.
- The value of an item equals or exceeds the amount owed against it.
- The debt should not be so high that repayment puts undue strain on the budget.

Let me give you an example of how a home mortgage might qualify. Historically, the home usually has been an appreciating asset, so it meets the first criteria. If you invest a reasonable down payment, you could expect to sell the home for at least enough to satisfy the mortgage, and this meets the second requirement. Lastly, the monthly house payment should not strain your budget.

If you meet the criteria and assume some "possible debt," I pray you will immediately establish the goal of eliminating even this debt. There is no assurance that the housing market will appreciate or even maintain current values. A loss of job can interrupt your income. Please consider paying off all debt.

HOW TO GET OUT OF DEBT

There are ten steps for getting out of debt. The steps are easy, but following them requires *hard work*. The goal is D-Day—Debtless Day when you become absolutely free of debt.

1. Pray

In 2 Kings 4:1-7 a widow was threatened with losing her children to her creditor, and she appealed to Elisha for help. Elisha instructed the widow to borrow many empty jars from her neighbors. The Lord supernaturally multiplied her only possession—a small quantity of oil—and all the jars were filled. She sold the increased oil and paid her debts to free her children.

The same God who provided supernaturally for the widow is interested in you becoming free from debt. The first step is to pray. Seek the Lord's help and guidance in your journey toward Debtless Day. He can either act immediately, as in the case of the widow, or slowly over time. In either case, prayer is essential.

A trend is emerging. As people begin to eliminate debt and to accelerate debt repayment, the Lord has blessed their faithfulness. Even if you can afford only a small monthly prepayment of your debt, please do it. The Lord can multiply your efforts.

2. Establish a Budget

In my experience, few people in debt have been using a budget. They may have had one—neatly filed away in a drawer or loaded on their computer— but they have not been using it. A budget helps you plan ahead, analyze your spending patterns and control the biggest budget buster of them all—impulse spending.

3. List Everything You Own

Evaluate your assets to determine if there is anything you do not need that might be sold to help you to get out of debt more quickly. What about that boat you no longer use? That set of golf clubs gathering dust in the garage? Is there anything you can sell to enable you to get out of debt?

Ziggy/Tom Wilson. Used by permission. United Press Syndicate.

4. List Everything You Owe

Many people, particularly if they owe a lot of money, do not know exactly what they owe. It must be human nature: If I avoid unpleasant things, perhaps they will go away. However, you must list your debts to determine your current financial situation. You also need to list the interest rate your creditors are charging for each debt.

5. Establish a Debt Repayment for Each Creditor

Part of the practical application this week is establishing a repayment schedule for each debt. I suggest you decide which debts to pay off first based on two factors:

- *Pay off small debts first.* Focus on paying off smaller debts first. You will be encouraged as they are eliminated, and this will free up cash to apply against other debts. After you pay off the first debt, apply its payment toward the next debt you wish to retire. After the second debt is paid off, apply what you were paying on the first and second debts toward the next debt you wish to eliminate, and so forth.
- *Pay off higher interest rate debts.* Determine what rate of interest you are being charged on each debt, and try to pay off first those that charge the highest rate of interest.

6. Consider Earning Additional Income

Many people hold jobs that simply do not produce enough income to meet their needs, even if they spend wisely. Two important issues about earning additional income: (1) Decide in advance to pay off debts with the added earnings. We tend to spend more than we make, whether we earn much or little. (2) Earn the additional income without harming your relationship with the Lord or with your family. If you are married, you may need to be creative in finding ways to involve the whole family in a job that brings the family together rather than tearing it apart.

7. Accumulate No New Debt

The only way I know to accumulate no additional debt is to pay for everything with cash or a check at the time of purchase. This raises the issue of credit cards. I do not believe that credit cards are inherently sinful, but they are dangerous. It is estimated that people carry more than 1 billion credit cards and only 40 percent of them are paid in full each month. People spend about one-third more when they use credit cards rather than cash, because they feel they are not really spending money (because it's just plastic). As one shopper said to another, "I like credit cards lots more than money, because they go so much further!"

When I analyze the finances of someone in debt, I use a simple rule of thumb to determine whether credit cards are too dangerous for them. If they do not pay the entire balance at the end of each month, I encourage them to perform some plastic surgery—any good scissors will do.

8. Be Content with What You Have

The advertising industry uses powerful, sophisticated methods of inducing the consumer to buy. Frequently the message is intended to create discontentment with what we have. A clear example is the American company that opened a new plant in Central America because the labor was plentiful and inexpensive. Everything progressed smoothly until the villagers received their first paycheck; afterwards they did not return to work. Several days later, the manager went down to the village chief to determine the cause of this problem, and the chief responded, "Why should we work? We already have everything we need." The plant stood idle for two months until someone came up with the bright idea of sending a mail-order catalogue to every villager. There has not been an employment problem since!

Note these three realities of our consumer-driven economy:

- The more television you watch, the more you spend.
- The more you look at catalogues and magazines, the more you spend.
- The more you shop, the more you spend.

Our family has been living proof of this. I could tell when my six-year-old daughter had been watching television, because suddenly she had to have a special glass from a fast-food restaurant. Limiting our television viewing also limits our wants.

There is an interesting passage in 1 Timothy 6:5-6: *"... men of depraved mind and deprived of the truth, who suppose that godliness is a means of gain. But godliness actually is a means of great gain, when accompanied by contentment."* I puzzled over this passage for the longest time, until I met a man who had recently come to know Christ. He told me that before he was introduced to Christ, he would take his date to the most expensive restaurants in town. But now that he is growing in his relationship with the Lord, he spends less. Because he is not trying to impress everyone, he can meet his friends at far less expensive places and concentrate on developing healthy relationships. Being content in Christ is a means of great gain.

People spend about one-third more when they use credit cards rather than cash.

9. Consider a Radical Change in Lifestyle

A growing number of people have lowered their standard of living significantly to get out of debt more quickly. Some have sold a home and moved to a smaller one or rented an apartment or moved in with family members. Many have sold automobiles with large monthly payments and have purchased inexpensive used cars for cash. In short, they have temporarily sacrificed their standard of living to be free from debt in a shorter period of time.

10. Do Not Give Up!

The last step is most difficult in getting out of debt. It takes hard work. These are three things you must do: (a) stop spending more than you are making. (b) pay the interest on the debt, (c) pay back what you have borrowed. It is never easy to get out of debt, but the freedom is worth the struggle.

Automobile loans are one of the leading causes of consumer indebtedness. Seventy percent of all the automobiles are financed. The average person keeps his car between three and four years. The average car lasts for twelve years.

Here's how to escape this trap. First of all, decide in advance to keep your car for at least six years. Secondly, pay off your automobile loan. Thirdly, continue paying the monthly car payment, but pay it to yourself. Pay it to a special savings account for your next car. Then, when you are ready to replace your car, the saved cash plus the trade-in should be sufficient to buy your car without credit. It may not be a new car, but you should be able to purchase a good, low-mileage used car, without any debt.

THE HOME MORTGAGE

I would like to challenge you to seek Christ and learn what He would have you do with your mortgage if you own a home. Is it possible that He may want you to pay off everything you owe, including your home mortgage? Obviously, paying off all debts, including the home mortgage, usually is a long-term goal because of the size of the average mortgage.

When Bev and I first learned God's financial principles, we began to explore what He wanted for us concerning debt. We felt we were to pay off everything, including the home mortgage. Frankly, this was an unrealistic goal for us at the time, but we began to explore how we might do it.

Let's examine the payment schedule for a home mortgage. Please do not let the size of the mortgage or the rate of interest hinder your thinking; this is for illustration purposes only. In the example below we are assuming a $100,000 mortgage at a 10 percent interest rate, paid over 30 years. The first year of the payment schedule (also known as an amortization schedule) would look like this:

PAYMENT # / MONTH		PAYMENT	INTEREST	PRINCIPAL	PRINCIPAL BALANCE
1	Jan	877.57	833.33	44.24	99,955.76
2	Feb	877.57	832.96	44.61	99,911.15
3	Mar	877.57	832.59	44.98	99,866.17
4	Apr	877.57	832.22	45.35	99,820.82
5	May	877.57	831.84	45.73	99,775.09
6	Jun	877.57	831.46	46.11	99,728.98
7	Jul	877.57	831.07	46.50	99,682.48
8	Aug	877.57	830.69	46.88	99,635.60
9	Sep	877.57	830.30	47.27	99,588.33
10	Oct	877.57	829.90	47.67	99,540.66
11	Nov	877.57	829.51	48.06	99,492.60
12	Dec	877.57	829.10	48.47	99,444.13
TOTALS FOR YEAR:		**10,530.84**	**9,974.97**	**555.87**	

As you can see, the payments during the early years are almost all interest. Of the $10,530.84 in house payments made this first year, only $555.87 went toward principal reduction! In fact, it will be 23 1/2 years before the principal and the interest portions of the payment equal each other! I don't know about you, but a 30-year goal to pay off my home mortgage doesn't excite me. If this can be reduced to 15 years, then the goal becomes much more attainable. There are several methods we can use to pay off the mortgage in half the time.

One method is to increase the amount of your monthly payment. In our example, a $100,000 mortgage at 10 percent interest payable over 30 years requires a monthly installment of $877.57. If you increase the monthly payment by $197.04 to $1,074.61, the mortgage will be paid in 15 years. During the 15 years you will have made $35,467 in advance payments on the principle. This will have saved you $122,495 in interest over the life of your mortgage.

A second method is to prepay the next month's principal payment in addition to your regular monthly payment of $877.57. By doing this consistently for 15 years you will have paid off the entire mortgage. Obviously, during the early years, the additional payment is low, but in the later years the extra payment will become substantial.

Study your mortgage to confirm that the mortgage may be prepaid without any penalty. A home mortgage usually allows such prepayment. And finally, let your lender know what you are planning. Not many borrowers prepay their mortgages, so he may be in shock for a while!

There are three primary arguments against this: (1) Why pay off a low-interest home mortgage when you can earn more elsewhere? (2) With inflation, the lender is being paid back with less valuable dollars during the life of the mortgage. (3) You are losing a tax shelter because the interest paid on a home mortgage is a tax deduction.

In spite of our tax structure, the Bible encourages savings and discourages debt.

Rather than addressing these arguments directly, we should recognize that our tax system is structured to reward indebtedness and penalize savings. We are taxed on interest earned, while interest paid on a home mortgage is treated as a tax deduction. However, in spite of our tax structure, the Bible encourages savings and discourages debt. Our purpose is simply to challenge you to seek Christ with an open heart to learn what He wants you to do.

For Bev and me, this turned into an exciting time as we began to pay off our mortgage. The Lord provided additional funds for us in an unexpected way, and today we do not owe anyone anything. This allowed me to take time off from my work to study and develop Crown materials. God may have something similar for you. Our living costs are more modest now than they were before, because we do not have debt or house payments.

INVESTMENT DEBT

Should you borrow money to make an investment? In my opinion, it is permissible to borrow for an investment, but only if you are not personally required to guarantee repayment of the debt. The investment for which you borrow (and any money invested as a down payment) should be the sole collateral for the debt. At first this may appear to contradict the biblical admonition for godly people to repay their debts. But let's explore this issue further.

For example, if we wanted to purchase a $70,000 rental house with $15,000 as the down payment, we would submit a loan application specifying the requirement of the house as sole security for the debt. We would explain to the lender that if, for any reason, we were unable to repay the loan, we would lose the $15,000 down payment, plus any other money we subsequently invested in the house, and the lender would own the house.

The lender must then make a business decision. Is a sufficient down payment invested? Is the house valuable enough? Is the housing market strong enough for the lender to feel secure about making the loan? In my opinion, the only circumstance under which we can be freed from the personal responsibility for a debt is when we have clearly communicated with the lender before obtaining the loan that we are not personally guaranteeing repayment of the loan.

Some have responded that it is impossible to locate a lender willing to loan without a personal guarantee. However, many later admitted they had not made a sincere effort to obtain such a loan. My response is, *"You do not have because you do not ask"* (James 4:2). Rarely have people made this an object of prayer. But I repeatedly have seen the Lord allow His children to secure this type of financing.

Be sure to limit your potential loss to the money you invested and the investment itself, because of the possibility of difficult financial events over which you have no control. It is painful to lose your investment, but it is much more serious to jeopardize meeting your family's needs by risking all your assets on investment debt. This position may appear too conservative. However, many people have become slaves of the lender and lost everything by guaranteeing debt on investments that went sour.

BUSINESS AND CHURCH DEBT

We also want to encourage you to pray about becoming debt-free in your business. Many are beginning to pay off all business-related debts, which helps establish a more financially stable enterprise.

Scripture does not specifically address whether a church may borrow money to build or expand its facility. If a church borrows, we recommend that it establishes a plan to pay off the debt as rapidly as possible. A growing number of churches have chosen to build without the use of any debt. For many of these churches the members have been encouraged and their faith increased as they have observed the Lord providing the necessary funds.

DEBT REPAYMENT RESPONSIBILITIES

Prompt Payment

Many delay payments to use the creditor's money as long as possible. There are seminars that actually teach people to live on the "ragged edge of being a dead beat," but this is not biblical. Proverbs 3:27-28 reads, *"Do not withhold good from those to whom it is due, when it is in your power to do it. Do not say to your neigh-bor, 'Go, and come back, and tomorrow I will give it,' when you have it with you."*

Godly people should pay their debts and bills as promptly as they can. We have a policy of trying to pay each bill the same day we receive it to demonstrate to others that knowing Jesus Christ has made us financially responsible.

Should You Use All Your Savings to Pay Off Debt?
It is wise not to deplete all your savings to pay off debt. Maintain a reasonable level of savings to provide for the unexpected. If you apply all your savings against debt and the unexpected does occur, you will probably be forced to incur more debt to fund the emergency.

Bankruptcy
A court can declare a person bankrupt and unable to pay his debts. Depending upon the type of bankruptcy, the court will either allow the debtor to develop a plan to repay his creditors, or the court will distribute his property among the creditors as payment for the debts.

A wave of bankruptcy is sweeping our country. Should a godly person declare bankruptcy? The answer is generally no. Psalm 37:21 tells us, *"The wicked borrows and does not pay back, but the righteous is gracious and gives."*

However, in our opinion, bankruptcy is permissible under two circumstances: a creditor forces a person into bankruptcy, or counselors believe the debtor's emotional health is at stake because of inability to cope with the pressure of creditors. For example, a husband may desert his wife and children, leaving her with business and family bills and debts for which she is responsible. She may not have the resources or job income to meet those obligations. The emotional trauma of an unwanted divorce, coupled with harassment from unsympathetic creditors, may be too much for her to bear.

After a person goes through bankruptcy, he should seek counsel from an attorney to determine if it's legally permissible to attempt to repay the debt even though he is not obligated to do so. If it is allowable, he should make every effort to repay the debt. For a large debt, this may be a long-term goal that is largely dependent on the Lord's supernaturally providing resources.

> *Godly people should pay their debts and bills as promptly as they can.*

COSIGNING

Cosigning relates to debt. Anytime you cosign, you become legally responsible for the debt of another. It is just as if you went to the bank, borrowed the money and gave it to your friend or relative who is asking you to cosign.

A Federal Trade Commission study found that 50 percent of those who cosigned for bank loans ended up making the payment. Seventy-five percent of those who cosigned for finance company loans ended up making the payments! Unfortunately, few cosigners plan for default. The casualty rate is so high because the professional lender has already determined that the loan is a bad risk. That is why he won't make the loan without someone who is financially responsible to guarantee it's repayment.

Fortunately, Scripture speaks very clearly about cosigning. Proverbs 17:18 reads, *"It is poor judgment to cosign another's note, to become responsible for his debts"* (LB). The words "poor judgment" are better translated "destitute of mind"!

A parent often cosigns for his or her child's first automobile. We decided not to do this. We wanted to model for our children the importance of not cosigning, and we wanted to discourage them from using debt. Instead, we trained them to plan ahead and save for the cash purchase of their first car.

Please use sound judgment and never cosign a note or become surety for any debt.

If you have already cosigned for a loan, the Scripture gives you direct counsel. Proverbs 6:1-5 reads, *"Son, if you endorse a note for someone you hardly know, guaranteeing his debt, you are in serious trouble. You may have trapped yourself by your agreement. Quick! Get out of it if you possibly can! Swallow your pride; don't let embarrassment stand in the way. Go and beg to have your name erased. Don't put it off. . . . if you can get out of this trap you have saved yourself like a deer that escapes from a hunter, or a bird from the net"* (LB).

COUNSEL
A Wise Person Seeks Advice

SOLOMON—
SOUGHT WISDOM FROM A MULTITUDE OF COUNSELORS

"The way of a fool is right in his own eyes,
but a wise man is he who listens to counsel."
Proverbs 12:15

COUNSEL HOMEWORK

 Scripture to Memorize:

> *"The way of a fool is right in his own eyes, but a wise man is he who listens to counsel"* (Proverbs 12:15).

 Practical Application: ☐ Complete the Estimated Budget.

DAY ONE

Read the Debt Notes on pages 39 to 50 and answer:

1. Are you in debt? If so, what steps do you sense the Lord wants you to take to become free of debt?

2. What did you learn about debt that proved to be especially helpful?

DAY TWO

Read *Proverbs 12:15*; *Proverbs 13:10*; and *Proverbs 15:22* and answer:

1. What are some of the benefits of seeking counsel?

   Proverbs 12:15—

   Proverbs 13:10—

   Proverbs 15:22—

2. What are some of the benefits you have experienced from seeking counsel?

3. What hinders you from seeking counsel?

DAY THREE

Read *Psalm 16:7* and *Psalm 32:8* and answer:

1. Does the Lord actively counsel His children?

Then read *Joshua 9:14-20* and *Psalm 106:13-15*.

2. What were the consequences of not seeking the Lord's counsel in these two passages?

Joshua 9:14-20—

Psalm 106:13-15—

3. Have you ever suffered for not seeking the Lord's counsel? If so, describe what happened.

4. How do you seek the Lord's counsel?

Read *Psalm 119:24; Psalm 119:105; 2 Timothy 3:16-17; and Hebrews 4:12.*

1. Should the Bible also serve as your counselor? Why?

Then read *Psalm 119:98-100.*

2. Living by the counsel of Scripture—

■ Makes us wiser than:

■ Gives us more insight than:

■ Gives us more understanding than:

3. Do you consistently read and study the Bible? If not, what prevents your consistency?

Read *Proverbs 1:8-9.*

1. Who should be among your counselors?

2. In your opinion, who should be the number-one human counselor of a husband? Of a wife? Why?

Read *Proverbs 11:14* and *Ecclesiastes 4:9-12*.

3. What do these verses communicate to you?

Proverbs 11:14—

Ecclesiastes 4:9-12—

4. How do you propose to apply this principle in your personal and/or business life?

DAY SIX

Read *Psalm 1:1-3* and answer:

1. Who should you avoid as a counselor?

2. What is your definition of a wicked person?

Then read *Proverbs 12:5*.

3. Why should you avoid their counsel?

4. Is there ever a circumstance in which you should seek the input of a person who does not know Christ? If so, when?

 Please write your prayer requests in your prayer log before coming to class.

 I will take the following action as a result of this week's study:

COUNSEL NOTES

Please do not read these notes until you completed the Counsel Homework.

COUNSEL NOTES

I frequently counsel people who have financial problems. Some of these people have lost everything and have subjected themselves and their families to years of heartache and stress. More often than not, they could have avoided their difficulties if before making the decisions that placed them in financial jeopardy, they had sought counsel from someone with a solid understanding of God's perspective of money.

SEEKING COUNSEL

Two common attitudes in our society keep us from seeking counsel. The first one is pride. Our culture perceives seeking advice as a sign of weakness. We are told, "Stand on your own two feet. You don't need anyone to help make your decisions for you!" Advertisers subtly encourage this because they know that the impulse sale often will be lost if the purchaser takes time to seek counsel. Secondly, is the attitude of willful stubbornness. This attitude is characterized by the statement, "Don't confuse me with the facts. My mind is already made up!" We often resist seeking counsel because we do not want to be confronted with the financial facts another person might discover. We don't want to be told we can't afford that beautiful, new car we already have decided to buy.

The admonitions from God's Word stand in stark contrast to the practice of not seeking counsel. Proverbs 19:20 reads, *"Listen to advice and accept instruction, and in the end you will be wise"* (NIV). And Proverbs 12:15 says, *"The way of a fool is right in his own eyes, but a wise man is he who listens to counsel."* I like Proverbs 10:8 from the Living Bible: *"The wise man is glad to be instructed, but a self-sufficient fool falls flat on his face."*

One seeks counsel to secure insights, suggestions and alternatives that will aid in making a proper decision. It is not the counselor's role to make the decision. You retain that responsibility.

Gather facts, but. . . .
We need to assemble the facts that will influence our decision, but we should not base our decision exclusively on those facts. We must determine specifically what the Lord wants us to do, and this may be contrary to what the facts alone would dictate.

This is clearly illustrated in Numbers 13 and 14. Moses sent twelve spies into the promised land. All of the spies came back with an identical assessment of the facts: It was a prosperous land, but terrifying giants lived there. Only two of the twelve spies, Joshua and Caleb, knew and believed what the Lord wanted them to do—to go in and possess the promised land. Because the children of Israel relied only on the tangible facts and did not act in faith on what the Lord wanted for them, they suffered 40 years of wandering in the wilderness until the entire generation had died.

SOURCES OF COUNSEL

What are the sources of counsel we need to seek? Before I make a financial decision, particularly an important one, I subject the decision to three sources of counsel.

THE COUNSEL OF SCRIPTURE

First, what does God's Word say about a particular issue? The Psalmist wrote, *"Your laws are both my light and my counselors"* (Psalm 119:24, LB). Psalm 119:98-100 reads, *"Your commandments make me wiser than my enemies, for they are ever mine. I have more insight than all my teachers, for Your testimonies are my meditation. I understand more than the aged, because I have observed Your precepts."*

Joshua and Caleb believed the counsel of God.

When we think of people who are skilled in financial decision making, we often think of teachers or those who are older and more experienced. Yet Scripture tells us we can have more insight and more wisdom than those who are educated and experienced in the ways of the world's economy by searching the Bible. I would rather obey the truth of Scripture than risk suffering the financial consequences of following my own inclinations or the opinions of people.

Moreover, the Bible makes this remarkable claim about itself: *"For the word of God is living and active and sharper than any two-edged sword . . . and . . . able to judge the thoughts and intentions of the heart"* (Hebrews 4:12). I have found this to be true. The Bible is a living book that our Lord uses to communicate His direction and truths which are relevant for all generations.

It may have come as a surprise to you to learn that the Bible contains 2,350 verses dealing with how we should handle money. The very first filter I put a financial decision through is Scripture. If the Scriptures clearly answer my question, I do not have to go any further, because the Bible contains the Lord's written, revealed will.

Bob and Barbara were faced with a difficult decision. Barbara's brother and his wife had just moved to Florida from Chicago. Because they experienced financial difficulties in Chicago, the bank would not loan them the money to purchase a home unless they had someone cosign the note. They asked Bob and Barbara to cosign. Barbara pleaded for Bob to do so; however, he was reluctant.

A friend referred them to the verses that warn against cosigning. When Barbara read the passages she responded, "Who am I to argue with God? We shouldn't cosign." Bob was tremendously relieved.

"Dear Lord, let me be the big cheese in the number-one job of the top outfit in the country, and let me come up with the right answers at the right times in the right places, but with it all, let me remain softspoken, country-shy, plain old Jeff Crotts from Spikard, Missouri."

Two years later, Barbara's brother and his wife were divorced and he declared bankruptcy. Can you imagine the strain on their marriage if Bob had cosigned that note? He might have said: "Barbara, I can't believe your brother did this to us! You got me into this! I tried not to cosign, but you forced me!" They probably would not have been able to survive financially.

If the Bible provides me clear direction in a financial matter, I know what to do. If the Bible is not specific about a particular issue, I subject my decision to the second source of counsel: godly people.

THE COUNSEL OF GODLY PEOPLE

"The godly man is a good counselor, because he is just and fair and knows right from wrong" (Psalm 37:30-31, LB). The Christian life is not one of independence from other Christians but of dependence upon one other. Nowhere is this illustrated more clearly than in Paul's discussion concerning the body of Christ in 1 Corinthians 12. Each of us is pictured as a different member of this body. Our ability to function normally is dependent upon the members working together. God has given each of us certain abilities and gifts, but God has not given any one person all the abilities that he needs to be most productive.

Spouse

If you are married, the first person you need to consult is your spouse. Frankly, it has been a humbling experience for me to seek the counsel of my wife, Bev, in financial matters, because she has no formal financial training. But she has saved me a great deal of money by her wise counsel.

I am occasionally exposed to investment opportunities. A slick salesman will tell me how I can make an investment that will be very profitable. I will get excited and go home to tell Bev about this terrific new investment. She will sit quietly and listen. Then she will say, "Howard, that sounds interesting, but I just don't feel good about it."

Women tend to be gifted with a wonderfully sensitive and intuitive nature that is usually very accurate. Men tend to focus objectively on the facts. The husband and wife need each other to achieve the proper balance for a correct decision. I also believe that the Lord honors the wife's "office" or "position" as helpmate to her husband. Many times the Lord communicates most clearly to the husband through his wife.

Husbands, let me be blunt. Regardless of her business background or her financial aptitude or even her apparent disinterest, you must cultivate and seek your wife's counsel. I have committed never to proceed with a financial decision in excess of $100 unless Bev agrees. There are additional benefits from seeking your spouse's counsel:

■ It will preserve your relationship!

The husband and wife should agree, because they both will experience the consequences of the decision. Even if their choice proves to be disastrous, their relationship remains intact. There are no grounds for an "I told you so" response.

■ It will honor your wife and prepare her for the future.

Unfortunately, some women in our culture suffer from a feeling of not being valuable. Seeking a wife's counsel will help enormously in her development of a healthy and proper self-esteem. When a husband seeks his wife's advice, he actually is communicating, "I love you. I respect you. I value your insight." Consistently asking for her advice also keeps your wife informed of your true financial condition. This is important in the event you predecease her or are unable to work. My father suffered a massive heart attack that incapacitated him for two years. Because he kept my mother informed about his business, she was able to step in and operate it successfully until he recovered.

"Now remember, John, no honey until you've finished all your locusts."

Parents

The second source of counsel is our parents. Proverbs 6:20-22 says, *"My son, observe the commandment of your father, and do not forsake the teaching of your mother; bind them continually on your heart; tie them around your neck. When you walk about, they will guide you; when you sleep, they will watch over you; and when you awake, they will talk to you."*

I cannot tell you how much I have benefited from the counsel of my father and mother. Our parents have the benefit of years of experience, they know us so well, and they have our best interest at heart.

In my opinion, we should seek their counsel even if they do not yet know Christ or have not been wise money managers themselves. Over the years, it's not uncommon for an unspoken barrier to be erected between a child and his parents. Asking their advice is a way to honor our parents and to build a bridge across any wall. It is a compliment for anyone to ask your advice—an expression of admiration. However, if you have not sought their counsel in a long time, start slowly! A word of caution: Genesis 2:24 reads, *"A man shall leave his father and his mother, and shall cleave to his wife; and they shall become one flesh."* Although the husband and wife should seek the counsel of their parents, the advice of the parents should be subordinate to the advice of the spouse, especially if a family conflict materializes.

Experienced People

We should also consult people experienced in the area in which we are attempting to make a decision. If I am considering a real estate investment, I attempt to locate the most qualified real estate investor to counsel me concerning the transaction. If I am going to purchase a car, I want to locate a trustworthy automobile mechanic and ask him to examine the car and give me his opinion before I complete the purchase.

COUNSEL NOTES

A Multitude of Counselors

Proverbs 15:22 reads, *"Without consultation, plans are frustrated, but with many counselors they succeed."* And Proverbs 11:14 says, *"Where there is no guidance, the people fall, but in abundance of counselors there is victory."* Each of us has a limited range of knowledge and experience; we need the input of others, who bring their own unique backgrounds to give us insight and broaden our thinking with alternatives we would never have considered without their advice.

I meet regularly with a small group who share their lives with one another and pray for each other. The members of this group know and understand each other well. Over the years, each person has been confronted with a difficult circumstance or major decision. We have observed that when someone is subjected to a painful circumstance, it is difficult to make wise, dispassionate decisions. We have experienced the benefits and safety of having a group of people who love one another, who know one another and who can give prayerful, objective counsel to one another even when it hurts. I am more receptive to constructive criticism when it comes from someone I respect and whom I know cares for me.

We also have learned that one major advantage of this close relationship is that we know many of each other's weaknesses and strengths. Because of this intimacy, it is easier to discern what direction the one seeking counsel should pursue.

Solomon describes the benefits of dependence upon one another in Ecclesiastes 4:9-12: *"Two are better than one because they have a good return for their labor. For if either of them falls, the one will lift up his companion. But woe to the one who falls when there is not another to lift him up. Furthermore, if two lie down together they keep warm, but how can one be warm alone? And if one can overpower him who is alone, two can resist him. A cord of three strands is not quickly torn apart."*

It can be very productive to gather your counselors together. Frequently the suggestions of one will trigger insights from another. What one says can be confirmed, disputed or discussed by the others. It is not uncommon for a clear direction or unanimous conclusion to be established when all of your counselors gather together.

When seeking a multitude of counselors, they often will not offer the same recommendations; in fact, there can be sharp disagreement. But usually a common thread will begin to develop, or sometimes each counselor will supply you with a different piece of the puzzle that you need to make the decision.

We strongly encourage you to include your pastor among your counselors, particularly when you are faced with a major decision.

THE COUNSEL OF THE LORD

During the process of analyzing the facts, searching the Bible, and obtaining the counsel of godly people, we need to be seeking direction from the Lord. This is the most important thing we can do. In Isaiah 9:6 we are told that one of the Lord's names is *"Wonderful Counselor."*

The Psalms also identify the Lord as our counselor. *"I [the Lord] will instruct you and teach you in the way which you should go; I will counsel you with My eye upon you"* (Psalm 32:8). *"You [the Lord] guide me with your counsel"* (Psalm 73:24, NIV). *"I will bless the Lord who has counseled me"* (Psalm 16:7).

In Scripture there are numerous examples of the unfortunate consequences of not seeking God's counsel and the blessings of heeding His counsel. After the children of Israel began their successful campaign to capture the promised land, some of the natives (Gibeonites) attempted to enter into a peace treaty with Israel. The Gibeonites deceived the leaders of Israel into believing they were from a distant land. Joshua 9:14-15 reads, *"So the men of Israel took some of their [Gibeonites] provisions and did not ask for the counsel of the Lord. And Joshua made peace with them and made a covenant with them, to let them live."*

The consequence of Israel not seeking the Lord's counsel was that the promised land remained populated with ungodly people, and Israel became ensnared by their false gods. The leaders were influenced by the "facts" they could see—facts that were designed to deceive them into thinking that the Gibeonites lived far away from the promised land. In many situations only the Lord can reveal to us real truth and proper direction. Only the Lord knows the future and the ultimate consequences of a decision.

A wonderful contrast is found in John 21:3-11. Peter and six of the other disciples fished all night long, but caught nothing. Jesus then came to the seashore and instructed them to cast their net on the right side of the boat. They responded out of obedience, and caught 153 large fish that did not break the net. When we know precisely what Christ wants us to do and we obey, it is much more productive than our efforts apart from the Lord's direction. In the process the net will not break, keeping the fabric of our relationship with the Lord and our family intact.

Throughout Scripture we are admonished to wait upon the Lord. Whenever you feel hurried or pressured or you experience a sense of confusion concerning a decision, discipline yourself to go to a quiet place that will allow you to listen prayerfully and quietly for His still, small voice. The world around you screams, "Hurry!" but the Lord tells you to wait.

AVOIDING THE COUNSEL OF THE WICKED

We need to avoid one particular source of counsel. *"How blessed is the man who does not walk in the counsel of the wicked"* (Psalm 1:1). The word "blessed" literally means to be "happy many times over." The definition of a "wicked" person is one who lives his life without regard to God. A wicked person can either be a person who does not yet personally know the Lord, or one who knows Jesus Christ as Savior but is not following Him in obedience. We should avoid the counsel of the wicked like the plague.

In my opinion, when you are searching for facts or technical expertise, it is permissible to seek input from those who may not know Christ—understanding that you are responsible to make the decision, even though you are going to consider their input.

GROW UP...QUIT WHINING...GET OUTTA HERE.

Fortune Tellers, Mediums, and Spiritualists

The Bible bluntly tells us never to seek the advice of fortune tellers, mediums, or spiritualists: *"Do not turn to mediums or spiritists; do not seek them out to be defiled by them. I am the Lord your God"* (Leviticus 19:31). Study this next passage carefully: *"So Saul died for his trespass which he committed against the Lord . . . and also because he asked counsel of a medium, making inquiry of it, and did not inquire of the Lord. Therefore He killed him"* (1 Chronicles 10:13-14). Saul died, in part, because he went to a medium. I believe, we should also avoid any methods they use in forecasting the future, such as horoscopes and all other practices of the occult.

Biased Counsel

We need to be cautious of the counsel of the biased. When receiving financial advice, ask yourself this question: "What stake does this person have in the outcome of my decision? Does he stand to gain or lose from this decision?" If the advisor will profit, be cautious when evaluating his counsel and always seek a second unbiased opinion.

A WORD TO THE COUNSELED

When you are seeking advice, supply your counselor with all the important facts. Do not attempt to manipulate your advisor to give the answer you want to hear by concealing pertinent information.

Major Decisions

Whenever you are faced with a major financial decision such as a job change or home purchase, it is helpful to go to a secluded place where you can spend uninterrupted time prayerfully reading Scripture and seeking the Lord. I encourage you to consider fasting during this time.

Know Your Counselors

Be selective in choosing your counselors. Make sure they have the courage to give you advice that may be contrary to your wishes, and attempt to include those who are gifted with wisdom. *"He who walks with wise men will be wise"* (Proverbs 13:20).

Continually ask the Lord for wisdom. *"But if any of you lacks wisdom, let him ask of God, who gives to all men generously and without reproach, and it will be given to him. But let him ask in faith without any doubting"* (James 1:5-6).

As you seek counsel, do not be surprised if the answer comes out of your own mouth. Interacting with others allows you the opportunity to verbalize thoughts and feelings that you may have never before expressed clearly.

COUNSEL NOTES

Counseling others can be a frustrating experience unless you have the proper understanding of the role of the counselor. Simply stated, the counselor should prayerfully and lovingly communicate the truth to the person seeking counsel, to the best of his ability and understanding, and leave the results to God. In the past I often would become involved emotionally in whether or not the person counseled would act on my recommendations. However, I discovered that some people are not yet prepared to follow advice. At other times I would discover later that my counsel was either inaccurate or incomplete. The counselor needs to be content knowing that the Lord is in control of every counseling experience.

Observe Strict Confidentiality
The person seeking advice needs to know that nothing he or she says will be communicated to another person without his or her prior permission. Only in this environment of trust will there be the candid dialogue that produces successful results.

When You Do Not Know
When the counselor is asked a question he does not know, he must be careful not to fabricate an answer. Simply respond with the truth: "I do not know." Often someone will come with a problem or circumstance that is outside of my experience. The best way to serve is to refer him or her to someone who has expertise in his or her area of need.

Simply stated, the counselor should prayerfully and lovingly communicate the truth to the person seeking counsel, to the best of his ability and understanding, and leave the results to God.

COUNSEL NOTES

DANIEL WAS HONEST

"They could find no ground of accusation or evidence of corruption, inasmuch as he was faithful, and no negligence or corruption was to be found in him" (Daniel 6:4).

"You shall not steal, nor deal falsely, nor lie to one another."
Leviticus 19:11

Scripture to Memorize:

"You shall not steal, nor deal falsely, nor lie to one another" (Leviticus 19:11).

Practical Application: ☐ Complete the Adjusting Your Budget practical application.

DAY ONE

Read the Counsel Notes on page 56 to 63 and answer:

1. What elements of God's perspective of counsel especially interested you?

2. Do you actively seek counsel when faced with a major financial decision? If not, how do you propose to do so in the future?

Read *Leviticus 19:11-13; Deuteronomy 25:13-16; Ephesians 4:25; and 1 Peter 1:15-16.*

1. What do these verses communicate to you about God's demand for honesty?

    Leviticus 19:11-13 —

    Deuteronomy 25:13-16 —

    Ephesians 4:25 —

    1 Peter 1:15-16 —

2. Are you consistently honest in even the smallest details? If not, what will you do to change?

3. What are two factors that motivate or influence us to act dishonestly?

    ■

    ■

4. How does this apply to you?

Read *Exodus 18:21-22* and answer:

1. Does the Lord require honesty for leaders? Why?

Then read *Proverbs 28:16* and *Proverbs 29:12*.

2. What are the consequences of dishonesty for people in leadership?

Proverbs 28:16 —

Proverbs 29:12 —

3. How does this apply to you?

DAY FOUR

Read *Proverbs 14:2* and answer:

1. Can you practice dishonesty and still love God? Why?

Then read *Proverbs 26:28* and *Romans 13:9-10*.

2. According to these passages, can you practice dishonesty and still love your neighbor? Why?

Read *Psalm 15:1-5; Proverbs 12:22; Proverbs 20:7;* **and** *Isaiah 33:15-16* **and answer:**

1. What are some of the benefits of honesty?

　　Psalm 15:1-5 —

　　Proverbs 12:22 —

　　Proverbs 20:7 —

　　Isaiah 33:15-16 —

Then read *Proverbs 3:32; Proverbs 13:11;* **and** *Proverbs 21:6.*

2. What are some of the curses of dishonesty?

　　Proverbs 3:32 —

　　Proverbs 13:11 —

　　Proverbs 21:6 —

Read *Exodus 22:1-4; Numbers 5:5-8;* **and** *Luke 19:8* **and answer:**

1. What does the Bible say about restitution?

2. If you have acquired anything dishonestly, how will you make restitution?

Then read *Exodus 23:8; Proverbs 15:27;* **and** *Proverbs 29:4.*

3. What is the biblical position on bribes?

4. Have you ever been asked to give or take a bribe? If so, describe what happened.

 Please write your prayer requests in your prayer log before coming to class.

 I will take the following action as a result of this week's study:

HONESTY NOTES

All of us have to make daily decisions about whether or not to handle money honestly. Do we tell the cashier at the grocery store when we receive too much change? Have you ever tried to sell something and been tempted not to tell the whole truth because you might have lost the sale?

HONESTY IN SOCIETY

These decisions are made more difficult because we live in what has been called the "Age of the Rip-off." It is an age in which employee theft is approaching $1 billion a week! It is an age in which an estimated 20 percent of the gross national product is unreported to the government! It is an age in which everyone around us seems to be acting dishonestly.

After pumping five dollars' worth of gas in my truck, I asked for a receipt, and the attendant made the receipt for ten dollars. When I pointed out the discrepancy, he replied, "Oh, just turn in the receipt to your company and you'll make a fast five bucks. After all, that's what many of the mailmen do in this area."

When I heard that, my heart sank. The verse that came immediately to mind was Judges 17:6, *"Every man did what was right in his own eyes."* That is precisely where we are today. We live in an age in which people formulate their own standards of honesty which change depending upon their circumstances.

We live in an age in which people formulate their own standards of honesty which change depending upon their circumstances.

HONESTY IN SCRIPTURE

God demands absolute honesty. Proverbs 20:23 reads, *"The Lord loathes all cheating and dishonesty"* (LB). And Proverbs 12:22 states, *"Lying lips are an abomination to the Lord."* And from Proverbs 6:16-17 we read, *"The Lord hates . . . a lying tongue."*

Study this comparison between what the Scriptures teach and what our society practices concerning honesty.

Issue	Scripture	Society
Standard of Honesty	Absolute	Relative
God's concern about honesty	He demands honesty	There is no God
The decision to be honest or dishonest is based upon:	Faith in the invisible, living God	Only the facts that can be seen
Question usually asked when deciding whether to be honest	Will it please God?	Will I get away with it?

The God of Truth

Truthfulness is one of God's characteristics. He is repeatedly identified as the God of truth. *"I am . . . the truth"* (John 14:6). Moreover, the Lord commands us to reflect His honest and holy character: *"Be holy yourselves also in all your behavior; because it is written, 'You shall be holy, for I am holy'"* (1 Peter 1:15-16).

In contrast to God's nature, John 8:44 describes the devil's character: *"He [the devil] was a murderer from the beginning, and does not stand in the truth, because there is no truth in him. Whenever he speaks a lie, he speaks from his own nature; for he is a liar, and the father of lies."* The Lord wants us to become conformed to His honest character rather than to the dishonest nature of the devil.

ABSOLUTE HONESTY

When being dishonest, we are acting as if the living God doesn't even exist! We believe that God is not able to provide exactly what we need, even though He has promised to do so.

God has imposed the standard of absolute honesty for Christians for the following reasons:

We Cannot Practice Dishonesty and Love God

Two of the Ten Commandments address honesty. *"You shall not steal. You shall not bear false witness against your neighbor"* (Exodus 20:15-16). And Jesus told us, *"If you love Me, you will keep My commandments"* (John 14:15).

We cannot disobey by practicing dishonesty and still love God. When being dishonest, we are acting as if the living God doesn't even exist! We believe that God is not able to provide exactly what we need, even though He has promised to do so (Matthew 6:33). We decide to take things into our own hands and do it our own dishonest way. We are also acting as if God is incapable of discovering our dishonesty and is powerless to discipline us. If we really believe God will discipline us, then we will not consider acting dishonestly.

Honest behavior is an issue of faith. An honest decision may look foolish in light of the circumstances we can observe, but the godly person knows Jesus Christ is alive, even though invisible. Every honest decision affirms and strengthens our faith in the living God and helps us grow into a closer relationship with Christ. However, if we choose to be dishonest we essentially deny our Lord and violate the first and greatest commandment. It is impossible to love God with all our heart, soul and mind if, at the same time, we are dishonest and act as if He does not exist. Scripture declares that the dishonest hate God. *"He who walks in his uprightness fears the Lord, but he who is crooked in his ways despises Him"* (Proverbs 14:2).

We Cannot Practice Dishonesty and Love Our Neighbor

The Lord demands absolute honesty because dishonest behavior also violates the second commandment, *"You shall love your neighbor as yourself"* (Mark 12:31). Romans 13:9-10 reads, *"If you love your neighbor as much as you love yourself, you will not want to harm or cheat him, or kill him or steal from him . . . love does no wrong to anyone"* (LB).

When we act dishonestly, we are stealing from another person. We may deceive ourselves into thinking it is a business, the government, or an insurance company that is suffering loss, but really it is the business owners, fellow taxpayers, or policy holders from whom we are stealing. It is just as if we took the money from their wallets. Dishonesty always injures people. The victim is always a person.

Credibility for Evangelism

Our Lord demands absolute honesty in handling money to enable us to demonstrate the reality of Jesus Christ to those who do not yet know Him.

I will never forget the first time I told a neighbor how he could come to know Christ as his personal Savior. He angrily responded, "Well, I know a man who always goes to church and talks a lot about Jesus, but watch out if you ever get in a business deal with him! He'd cheat his own grandmother! If that's what it means to be a Christian, I don't want any part of it!"

Our actions speak louder than our words. Scripture says to *"prove yourselves to be blameless and innocent, children of God above reproach in the midst of a crooked and perverse generation, among whom you appear as lights in the world"* (Philippians 2:15).

We can influence people **for** Jesus Christ by handling our money honestly. Robert Newsom had been trying to sell an old pickup truck for months. Finally, an interested buyer decided to purchase the truck. However, at the last moment he said, "I'll buy this truck, but only on one condition — you don't report this sale so I won't have to pay state sales tax."

Although he was tempted, Robert responded, "I'm sorry, I can't do that because Jesus Christ is my Lord." Robert later said, "You should have seen the buyer's reaction. He almost went into shock! Then an interesting thing happened. His attitude completely changed. Not only did he purchase the truck, but he eagerly joined my wife and me around our dinner table. Rarely have I seen anyone as open to the truth about knowing Jesus Christ in a personal way."

Because Robert had acted honestly even though it was going to cost him money (*"Prove yourselves to be blameless and innocent, children of God above*

"If you love your neighbor as much as you love yourself, you will not want to harm or cheat him, or kill him or steal from him . . . love does no wrong to anyone."

ROMANS 13:9-10

Choosing to walk the narrow path of honesty eliminates the many possible avenues of dishonesty. Decision making becomes simpler because the honest path is a clear path.

reproach"), he had demonstrated to this person (*"a crooked and perverse generation"*) the reality of a personal faith in Jesus Christ (*"appear as lights in the world"*).

Confirms God's Direction

Proverbs 4:24-26 reads, *"Put away from you a deceitful mouth, and put devious lips far from you. Let your eyes look directly ahead, and let your gaze be fixed straight in front of you. Watch the path of your feet and all your ways will be established."* What a tremendous principle. As you are absolutely honest, *"all your ways will be established."* Choosing to walk the narrow path of honesty eliminates the many possible avenues of dishonesty. Decision-making becomes simpler because the honest path is a clear path.

"If only I had understood that truth," Raymond wept. "But Donna and I wanted that house so much. It was our dream house. However, our existing debts were so large that we couldn't qualify for the mortgage. The only way for us to buy the house was to hide some of our debts from the bank.

"It was the worst decision of my life. Almost immediately we were unable to meet the mortgage payment and pay our other debts too. The pressure built and was almost more than Donna could stand. Our dream house ended up causing a family nightmare. I not only lost the home, but nearly lost my wife."

Had Raymond and Donna been honest, the bank would not have approved the loan. They would not have been able to purchase that particular home. Had they prayed and waited, perhaps the Lord would have brought something more affordable, thus avoiding the pressure that almost ended their marriage. Honesty helps confirm God's direction.

My business used to be real estate development. Normally, several years lapsed between the inception of a project and its completion. Our economy can change radically during that time. What might appear to be a sensible project in the beginning could become a disaster. When considering a new development, I would pray, "Lord, show me clearly if You want me involved, but shut the door if You don't." I wanted to be certain God's sovereign hand was providing that opportunity. I would never know if God had wanted to shut the door if I had forced it open by being dishonest.

Even Small Acts of Dishonesty Are Harmful

God requires us to be **absolutely honest**, because even the smallest act of dishonesty is sin. And even the smallest sin interrupts our fellowship with the Lord and retards our maturity in Christ. The smallest "white lie" will harden our hearts, making our consciences increasingly insensitive to sin and deafening our ears to the still small voice of the Lord. This single cancer cell of small dishonesty multiplies and spreads to greater dishonesty. *"Whoever is dishonest with very little, will also be dishonest with much"* (Luke 16:10, NIV).

An event in Abraham's life has challenged me to be honest in small matters. In Genesis 14 the king of Sodom offered Abraham all the goods Abraham recovered when he returned from successfully rescuing the people of Sodom. But Abraham responded to the king, *"I have sworn to the Lord God Most High, possessor of heaven and earth, that I will not take a thread or a sandal thong or anything that is yours"* (Genesis 14:22-23).

Just as Abraham was unwilling to take so much as a thread or a sandal thong, I challenge you to make a similar commitment in this area of honesty. Covenant not to steal a stamp or a photocopy or a paper clip or a long distance telephone call or a penny from your employer, the government or anyone else. The people of God must be honest in even the smallest matters.

To love God and our neighbor, to evangelize effectively, to confirm God's direction and to develop a heart sensitive to God—is there any wonder that our Lord has imposed the standard of absolute honesty?

ESCAPING THE TEMPTATION OF DISHONESTY

A friend was teaching these principles in a secular school when one student raised his hand and said, "I think we all would like to be the person you're talking about, but I know in my heart that if the right opportunity comes along, I'm going to be dishonest." I think he is correct. Apart from denying ourselves and living our lives yielded to the Holy Spirit, all of us will be dishonest.

"Live by the Spirit, and you will not gratify the desires of the sinful nature. For the sinful nature desires what is contrary to the Spirit, and the Spirit what is contrary to the sinful nature" (Galatians 5:16-17, NIV).

The character of our human nature is to act dishonestly. *"Out of men's hearts come evil thoughts . . . theft . . . deceit"* (Mark 7:21-22, NIV). The desire of the Spirit is for us to be absolutely honest. I can't overemphasize that the absolutely honest life is supernatural. We must submit ourselves entirely to Jesus Christ as Lord and allow Him to live His life through us. There is no other way.

I heartily recommend you read a short book by Andrew Murray titled *Humility*. It is an excellent and motivating study for living your life yielded to Christ as Lord.

The following principles will help you to develop the habit of honesty:

1. By Practicing the Golden Rule
"Do not merely look out for your own personal interests but also for the interests of others" (Philippians 2:4). This verse is better translated, "look intently" after the interests of others. The Lord confronted me through this passage and pointed out my self-centeredness and lack of concern for others just when I was about to purchase some land. The seller was not a real estate expert and knew nothing of its value. I had been secretly congratulating myself because I knew the purchase price I was offering was too low. Not once had I even considered what would be fair to the seller. I had concentrated solely on acquiring the property at the lowest possible price.

I re-examined the transaction in the light of "looking intently" after the seller's interests as well as my own. After an intense inner struggle, I concluded that I should pay more for the property to reflect its true value. Practicing the

Golden Rule is sometimes costly, but its reward is a clear conscience before God and other people.

2. By a Healthy Fear of the Lord

When I talk of a "healthy fear" of the Lord, I do not mean that God is a big bully just waiting for the opportunity to punish us; rather He is a loving Father who, out of infinite love, disciplines His children for their benefit. *"He disciplines us for our good, that we may share His holiness"* (Hebrews 12:10).

One of the methods God uses to motivate us to honest living is this "healthy fear." Proverbs 16:6 reads, *"By the fear of the Lord one keeps away from evil."* Let me illustrate how the fear of the Lord helps us act honestly. I once shared a motel room with a friend. As we were leaving, he slipped one of the motel's drinking glasses into his pocket and walked to the car. Suddenly, I felt the fear of the Lord. What came to mind was Hebrews 12:11, *"All discipline for the moment seems not to be joyful, but sorrowful."* Discipline hurts! Given the choice, I would much rather obey His Word than to make a deliberate decision that would prompt my loving Father to discipline me. I was afraid for my friend and for myself as an accomplice.

Moreover, I believe our heavenly Father will not allow us to keep anything we have acquired dishonestly. Proverbs 13:11 reads, *"Wealth obtained by fraud dwindles."*

A friend purchased four azalea plants but the check-out clerk had only charged her for one. She knew it, but she left the store anyway without paying for the other three. She told me it was miraculous how quickly three of those plants died! Think about this for a moment: If you are a parent and one of your children steals something, do you allow the child to keep it? Of course not. You require its return because the child's character would be destroyed if he kept stolen property. Not only do you insist on its return, but you usually want the child to experience enough discomfort to produce a lasting impression. For instance, you might have the child confess the theft to the store manager. When our heavenly Father lovingly disciplines us, it is usually done in such a way that we will not forget. This can be painful or embarrassing.

You can imagine how relieved I was when my friend returned the motel's glass!

3. By Staying Away from Dishonest People

Scripture teaches that we are deeply influenced by those around us, either for good or evil. David recognized this and said, *"My eyes shall be upon the faithful of the land, that they may dwell with me; he who walks in a blameless way is the one who will minister to me. He who practices deceit shall not dwell within my house; he who speaks falsehood shall not maintain his position before me"* (Psalm 101:6-7). Paul wrote, *"Do not be deceived: 'Bad company corrupts good morals'"* (1 Corinthians 15:33). Solomon was even stronger: *"He who is a partner with a thief hates his own life"* (Proverbs 29:24).

Obviously, we are not to isolate ourselves from every dishonest person. In fact, we are to be salt and light in the world. We should, however, be very cautious when choosing our close friends or considering a business relationship with another.

Choosing to walk the narrow path of honesty eliminates the many possible avenues of dishonesty. Decision making becomes simpler because the honest path is a clear path.

HONESTY NOTES

If I observe a person who is dishonest in his dealings with the government or in a small matter, I know this person will be dishonest in greater matters and probably in his dealings with me. In my opinion, it is impossible for a person to be selectively honest. Either the person has made the commitment to be absolutely honest or his dishonesty will become more prevalent. It is much easier to remain absolutely honest if you are surrounded by others who are of a like mind and conviction.

4. By Giving

We can escape the temptation of acting dishonestly by giving generously to those in need. *"Let him who steals steal no longer, but rather let him labor performing with his own hands what is good in order that he may have something to share with him who has need"* (Ephesians 4:28).

As we give, it draws us closer to Christ and reduces our incentive to steal. After all, if we are going to give something away, there's not much reason to steal it!

WHAT TO DO WHEN WE HAVE BEEN DISHONEST

Unfortunately, from time to time, we will act dishonestly, but once we recognize that we have, we need to do the following:

1. Restore Our Fellowship with God

Anytime we sin we break our fellowship with our Lord, and this needs to be restored. First John 1:9 tells us how: *"If we confess our sins, He is faithful and righteous to forgive us our sins and to cleanse us from all unrighteousness."* We must agree with God that our dishonesty was sin, and then thankfully accept God's gracious forgiveness so we can again enjoy His fellowship.

2. Restore Our Fellowship with the Harmed Person

After our fellowship with Christ has been restored, we need to confess our dishonesty to the person we offended. *"Confess your sins to one another"* (James 5:16).

Ouch! This hurts. I've had only a handful of people confess that they have wronged me. Interestingly, these are the very people who have become some of my closest friends, in part because of my respect for them. They so desired an honest relationship with me that they were willing to expose their sins.

This has been very hard for me. For the first time, several years ago I went to someone I had wronged and confessed my sin . . . not that I hadn't had plenty of opportunities before! In the past, however, my pride stood in the way. Afterward I sensed a great freedom in our relationship. I also discovered that, because it is a painfully humbling experience, confession helps break the habit of dishonesty.

If I observe a person who is dishonest in his dealings with the government or in a small matter, I know this person will be dishonest in greater matters and probably in his dealings with me.

A person's lack of financial prosperity may be a consequence of violating this principle. *"He who conceals his transgressions will not prosper, but he who confesses and forsakes them will find compassion"* (Proverbs 28:13).

3. Restore Dishonestly Acquired Property

If we have acquired anything dishonestly, we must return it to its rightful owner. *"Then it shall be, when he sins and becomes guilty that he shall restore what he took by robbery . . . or anything about which he swore falsely; he shall make restitution for it in full, and add to it one-fifth more. He shall give it to the one to whom it belongs"* (Leviticus 6:4-5).

Restitution is a tangible expression of repentance and an effort to correct a wrong. Zaccheus is a good example. He promised Jesus, *"If I have defrauded anyone of anything, I will give back four times as much"* (Luke 19:8).

If it's not possible for restitution to be made, then the property should be given to the Lord. Numbers 5:8 teaches, *"But if the man has no relative to whom restitution may be made for the wrong, the restitution which is made for the wrong must go to the Lord for the priest."*

Zaccheus

HONESTY REQUIRED FOR LEADERS

The Lord is especially concerned with the honesty of leaders.

Influence of Leaders

Leaders influence those who follow them. The owner of a trucking business began wearing cowboy boots to work. Within six months, all the men in his office were in boots. He suddenly changed to a traditional business shoe and six months later all the men were wearing business shoes.

In a similar way, a dishonest leader produces dishonest followers. *"If a ruler pays attention to falsehood, all his ministers become wicked"* (Proverbs 29:12). The leader of a business, church or home must set the example of honesty in his or her personal life before those under his or her authority can be expected to do the same.

The president of a large international construction company was once asked why his company did not work in countries where bribes were a way of life. He responded, "We never build in those countries, no matter how profitable the project may appear, because we can't afford to. If my employees know we are acting dishonestly, they will eventually become thieves. Their dishonesty will ultimately cost us more than we could ever earn on a project."

During an effort to reduce expenses, a company discovered the employees were making frequent, personal, long-distance telephone calls at the office and charging them to the company. The company president had unwittingly fueled this problem. He had reasoned that because he placed approximately the same number of company long-distance calls on his home phone as personal long-distance calls on the company phone, a detailed accounting was unnecessary. His employees, however, knew only of his calls at work. They concluded that if this dishonest practice was acceptable for the boss, it was acceptable for all. A leader should *"abstain from all appearance of evil"* (1 Thessalonians 5:22, KJV), because his or her actions influence others.

Selection of Leaders

Dishonesty should disqualify a person from leadership. Listen to the counsel of Jethro, Moses' father-in-law: *"You shall select out of all the people able men who fear God, men of truth, those who hate dishonest gain; and you shall place these . . . as leaders of thousands, of hundreds, of fifties and of tens"* (Exodus 18:21). Two of the four criteria for leadership selection that Jethro gave Moses dealt with honesty—*"men of truth, those who hate dishonest gain."* I believe the Lord wants us to continue to select leaders on the basis of these same character qualities.

Preservation of Leaders

Not only are leaders selected in part by honest behavior, but a leader retains his position by honest behavior. *"A leader . . . who hates unjust gain will prolong his days"* (Proverbs 28:16). We have all witnessed the leaders of business or government who have been demoted because of a root problem of personal corruption.

How can a leader maintain the standard of absolute honesty? By becoming accountable. It is necessary to establish a system of checks and balances which do not usurp the leader's authority but which provide a definite structure to insure that the leader is accountable.

BRIBES

A bribe is defined as anything given to a person to influence him to do something illegal or wrong. The taking of bribes is clearly prohibited in Scripture: *"And you shall not take a bribe, for a bribe blinds the clear-sighted and subverts the cause of the just"* (Exodus 23:8). Bribes are often disguised as a "gift" or "referral fee." Evaluate any such offer to confirm that it is not in reality a bribe.

BLESSINGS AND CURSES

Listed on the next page are some of the blessings the Lord has promised for the honest and some of the curses reserved for the dishonest. Read these slowly and prayerfully, asking God to use His Word to motivate you to a life of honesty.

BLESSINGS FOR THE HONEST:

- Blessing of a more intimate relationship with the Lord. *"For the crooked man is an abomination to the Lord; but He is intimate with the upright"* (Proverbs 3:32).

- Blessings on the family. *"A righteous man who walks in his integrity— how blessed are his sons after him"* (Proverbs 20:7).

- Blessings of life. *"Truthful lips will be established forever; but a lying tongue is only for a moment"* (Proverbs 12:19).

- Blessings of prosperity. *"Much wealth is in the house of the righteous, but trouble is in the income of the wicked"* (Proverbs 15:6).

CURSES RESERVED FOR THE DISHONEST:

- Curse of alienation from God. *"For the crooked man is an abomination to the Lord"* (Proverbs 3:32).

- Curse on the family. *"He who profits illicitly troubles his own house, but he who hates bribes will live"* (Proverbs 15:27).

- Curse of death. *"The getting of treasures by a lying tongue is a fleeting vapor; the pursuit of death"* (Proverbs 21:6).

- Curse of poverty. *"Wealth obtained by fraud dwindles"* (Proverbs 13:11).

GIVING
Giving is Blessed

JESUS COMMENDS SACRIFICAL GIVING—
*"A poor widow came in and put in two small copper coins which amount to a cent.
And calling His disciples to Him, He said to them, 'This poor widow put in more
than all the contributors to the treasury; for they all put in out of their surplus,
but she, out of her poverty, put in all she owned, all she had to live on.'"*

Mark 12:42-44

*"Remember the words of the Lord Jesus, that He Himself said,
'It is more blessed to give than to receive.'"*
Acts 20:35

Scripture to Memorize:

"Remember the words of the Lord Jesus, that He Himself said, 'It is more blessed to give than to receive'" (Acts 20:35).

 Practical Application: ☐ Complete the *Beginning Your Budget* practical application.

DAY ONE

Read the *Honesty Notes* on pages 71 to 80 and answer:

1. How does the example of Abraham in *Genesis 14:21-23* challenge you to be honest?

2. Ask the Lord to reveal any areas of dishonesty in your life. How do you propose to deal with these areas?

DAY TWO

Read *Matthew 23:23; 1 Corinthians 13:3;* and *2 Corinthians 9:7* and answer:

1. What do each of these passages communicate about the importance of the proper attitude in giving?

   Matthew 23:23—

   1 Corinthians 13:3—

   2 Corinthians 9:7—

2. How do you think a person can develop the proper attitude in giving?

3. After prayerfully evaluating your attitude in giving, how would you describe it?

DAY THREE

Read *Acts 20:35* and answer:

1. How does this principle from God's economy differ from the way most people view giving?

2. List the benefits for the giver, which are found in each of the following passages:

Proverbs 11:24-25—

Matthew 6:20—

Luke 12:34—

1 Timothy 6:18-19—

DAY FOUR

Read *Genesis 14:20* and answer:

1. How much did Abraham give? Was his gift prior to the Old Testament Law?

Then read Malachi 3:8-10.

2. Was the tithe required under Old Testament Law?

Then read 2 Corinthians 8:1-5.

3. Identify three principles from this passage that should influence how much you give.

■

■

■

Prayerfully (with your spouse if you are married) seek the Lord's guidance to determine how much you should give. You will not be asked to disclose the amount.

DAY FIVE

Read *Matthew 15:4-6* **and** *1 Timothy 5:8* **and answer:**

1. Does the Bible require us to take care of our family members? How does this apply to you?

Then read *Numbers 18:8-10,24; Galatians 6:6*; **and** *1 Timothy 5:17-18.*

2. What do these verses tell you about financially supporting your church and those who teach the Scriptures?

   Numbers 18:8-10,24—

   Galatians 6:6—

   1 Timothy 5:17-18—

Read *Isaiah 58:6-11* **and** *Ezekiel 16:49* **and answer:**

1. What do these verses say about giving to the poor?

    Isaiah 58:6-11—

    Ezekiel 16:49—

Then study *Matthew 25:35-45.*

2. How does Jesus Christ identify with the poor?

Then read *John 13:27-29* **and** *Galatians 2:9-10.*

3. What do these verses communicate to you about giving to the poor?

    John 13:27-29—

    Galatians 2:9-10—

4. Are you currently giving to the poor? If not, what is hindering you?

 Please write your prayer requests in your prayer log before coming to class.

 I will take the following action as a result of this week's study:

GIVING NOTES

Please do not read these notes until you completed the Giving Homework.

Because God loved He gave. Because God is love, He is also a giver.

F ew areas of the Christian life can be more frustrating than that of giving. For several years after I met Christ, I did not want to give. I would go to almost any length to avoid it. On a few occasions, I found myself in a position in which I felt obligated to give in order to appear spiritual. I did so, but my heart wasn't in it.

My whole perspective changed once I learned what the Bible actually taught. I wanted to give, however, I was frustrated by another problem: an unlimited number of needs and my limited resources. How could I decide to whom to give? My church, the hungry poor, campus and prison ministries, missionary efforts, radio and television programs, and many other vital ministries needed financial support.

These decisions are even more difficult because of today's intense competition for a Christian's money. It seems as if my mailbox is constantly full of appeals. I react to these requests with mixed emotions—compassion, gratitude, despair, guilt, and even cynicism. I feel deep compassion when confronted with those facing starvation of body or spirit. I am grateful that there are people whose life purpose is to meet those needs. I almost despair at the unbelievable needs of those less fortunate than ourselves. I feel guilty that perhaps we are not giving enough. And I become cynical at being solicited for more and more money, and perhaps being manipulated by people whose goals may be worthwhile, but whose means of achieving those goals are questionable.

We will examine the four elements of giving: attitudes, advantages, amount, and approach.

ATTITUDES IN GIVING

God evaluates our actions on the basis of our attitude. God's attitude toward giving is best summed up in John 3:16: *"For God so loved the world, that He gave His only begotten Son."* Note the sequence. Because God loved, He gave. Because God is love, He is also a giver. He set the example of giving motivated by love.

An attitude of love in giving is crucial: *"If I give all my possessions to feed the poor . . . but do not have love, it profits me nothing"* (1 Corinthians 13:3). It is difficult to imagine anything more commendable than giving everything to the poor. However, giving with the wrong attitude, without love, is of no benefit to the giver.

In God's economy the attitude is more important than the amount. Jesus

Reprinted from *Off the Church Wall* by Rob Portlock. ©1987 by Rob Portlock. Used by permission of Intervarsity Press. P.O. Box 1400 Downers Grove, IL 60515

emphasized this in Matthew 23:23: *"Woe to you, scribes and Pharisees, hypocrites! For you tithe mint and dill and cummin, and have neglected the weightier provisions of the law: justice and mercy and faithfulness; but these are the things you should have done without neglecting the others."* The Pharisees had been careful to give the correct amount—down to the last mint leaf in their gardens. However, Christ rebuked them because He looks past the amount of the gift to the heart of the giver.

Our basis for giving out of a heart filled with love is that our gifts are actually given to the Lord Himself. An example of this is found in Numbers 18:24: *"For the tithe of the sons of Israel, which they offer as an offering to the Lord, I have given to the Levites for an inheritance."* If giving is merely to a church, a ministry, or a needy person, it is only charity. But if it is given to the Lord, it becomes an act of worship. Because God is our Creator, our Savior, and our faithful Provider, we can express our gratefulness and love by giving our gifts to Him.

For example, when the offering plate is being passed at church, we should consciously remind ourselves that we are giving our gift to the Lord Himself.

In addition to giving out of a heart filled with love, we are to give cheerfully. *"Let each one do just as he has purposed in his heart; not grudgingly or under compulsion; for God loves a cheerful giver"* (2 Corinthians 9:7). The original Greek word for cheerful is "Hilarios," which is translated into the English word hilarious. We are to be hilarious givers over the prospect of giving.

Unfortunately, there is usually little hilarity in the pews when the offering plate is passed in church. In fact, the atmosphere more often reminds us of a patient waiting in the dentist chair who knows a painful extraction is about to occur.

How do we develop this hilarity in our giving? Consider the early churches of Macedonia. *"Now, brethren, we wish to make known to you the grace of God which has been given in the churches of Macedonia, that in a great ordeal of affliction their abundance of joy and their deep poverty overflowed in the wealth of their liberality"* (2 Corinthians 8:1-2).

How did the Macedonians, who were in terrible circumstances, *"their great affliction and deep poverty,"* still manage to give with an *"abundance of joy"*? The answer is in verse 5: *"They first gave themselves to the Lord and to us by the will of God."* The key to cheerful giving is to submit yourself to Christ. Ask Him to direct how much He wants you to give. Only then are we in a position to reap any of the advantages by giving with the proper attitude.

Stop and examine yourself. What is your attitude toward giving?

ADVANTAGES OF GIVING

"What's this we hear about you laying up treasures in heaven?"

Obviously a gift benefits the recipient. The church continues its ministry, the hungry are fed, the naked are clothed and missionaries are sent. But incredibly, according to God's economy, when a gift is given with the proper attitude it benefits the giver more than the receiver. *"Remember the words of the Lord Jesus, that He Himself said, 'It is more blessed to give than to receive'"* (Acts 20:35). As we examine Scripture, we find that the giver benefits in four significant areas:

1. Increase in Intimacy

Above all else, giving directs our attention and heart to Christ. Matthew 6:21 tells us, *"For where your treasure is, there will your heart be also."* This is why it is so necessary to give each gift to the person of Jesus Christ. When you give your gift to Him, your heart will automatically be drawn to the Lord.

Also remember that giving is one of the nine responsibilities of the steward, and the more faithful we are in the discharge of these responsibilities, the more we can *"enter into the joy of our Master."* Nothing in life can compare to entering into His joy and knowing Christ more intimately.

2. Increase in Character

Our heavenly Father wants us as His children to be conformed to the image of His Son. The character of Christ is that of an unselfish giver. Unfortunately, humans are by nature selfish. One of the key ways we become conformed to Christ is by regular giving. Someone once said, "Giving is not God's way of raising money; it is God's way of raising people into the likeness of His Son."

3. Increase in Heaven

Matthew 6:20 reads, *"But lay up for yourselves treasures in heaven, where neither moth nor rust destroys, and where thieves do not break in and steal."* The Lord tells us that there really is something akin to the "First National Bank of Heaven." He wants us to know that we can invest for eternity.

Paul wrote, *"Not that I seek the gift itself, but I seek for the profit which increases to your account"* (Philippians 4:17). There is an account for each of us in heaven which we will be able to enjoy for eternity. And while it is true

GIVING NOTES

that we "can't take it with us," Scripture teaches that we can make deposits to our heavenly account before we die.

4. Increase on Earth

Many people do not believe that giving results in material blessings flowing to the giver. But study the following passages:

Proverbs 11:24-25 reads, *"There is one who scatters, yet increases all the more, and there is one who withholds what is justly due, but it results only in want. The generous man will be prosperous, and he who waters will himself be watered."*

Examine 2 Corinthians 9:6-11: *"Now this I say, he who sows sparingly shall also reap sparingly; and he who sows bountifully shall also reap bountifully . . . God is able to make all grace abound to you, that always having all sufficiency in everything, you may have an abundance for every good deed; as it is written, 'He scattered abroad, He gave to the poor, His righteousness abides forever.' Now He who supplies seed to the sower and bread for food, will supply and multiply your seed for sowing and increase the harvest of your righteousness; you will be enriched in everything for all liberality."*

These verses clearly teach that giving results in a material increase: *". . . shall also reap bountifully . . . always having all sufficiency in everything . . . may have an abundance . . . will supply and multiply your seed . . . you will be enriched in everything."*

But note carefully **why** the Lord is returning an increase materially: *"Always having all sufficiency in everything, you may have an abundance for every good deed . . . will supply and multiply your seed for sowing . . . you will be enriched in everything for all liberality."* As shown in the diagram below the Lord produces a material increase so that we may give more and have our needs met at the same time.

Study the cycle in giving:

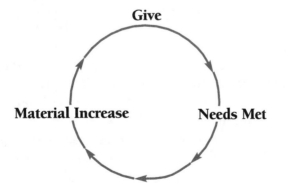

One reason the Lord reveals that a gift will result in material increase is because He wants us to recognize He is sovereignly behind the multiplication of our resources. God has chosen to be invisible, but He wants us to experience His reality.

When we give, we should do so with a sense of anticipating the Lord to provide a material increase, even though we do not know when or how the Lord may choose to provide this increase. From my experience, He can be

When we give, we should do so with a sense of anticipating the Lord to provide a material increase, even though we do not know when or how the Lord may choose to provide this increase. From my experience, He can be very creative!

very creative! Remember, the giver can reap the advantages of giving only when he or she gives cheerfully out of a heart filled with love, not when the motive of giving is just to get.

AMOUNT TO GIVE

Let's survey what the Scripture says about how much to give. Before the Old Testament Law was given there were two instances of giving with a known amount. In Genesis 14:20 Abraham gave ten percent, a tithe, of the spoils to Melchizedek after the rescue of his nephew Lot. And in Genesis 28:22, Jacob promised to give the Lord a tenth of all his possessions if God brought him safely through his journey.

After the Law was given a tithe was required. The Lord condemns the children of Israel in Malachi 3:8-9 for not tithing properly: *"Will a man rob God? Yet you are robbing Me! But you say, 'How have we robbed You?' In tithes and offerings. You are cursed with a curse, for you are robbing Me, the whole nation of you!"*

In addition to the tithe there were various offerings. The Lord also made special provisions for the needs of the poor. Every seven years all debts were forgiven, every 50 years the land was returned to the original land-owning families, and there were special rules for harvesting that allowed the poor to glean behind the harvesters. Ruth is an example of a needy person who gleaned in the field of Boaz.

God made another significant provision for the poor in Deuteronomy 15:7-8: *"If there is a poor man with you, one of your brothers, in any of your towns in your land which the Lord your God is giving you, you shall not harden your heart, nor close your hand from your poor brother; but you shall freely open your hand to him, and shall generously lend him sufficient for his need in whatever he lacks."* Even under the law the extent of one's giving was not limited by a fixed percentage but was in part dictated by the material needs of the surrounding people.

The New Testament teaches that we are to give in proportion to the material blessing we receive, it also commends sacrificial giving.

What I like about the tithe is that it is systematic, and the amount of the gift is easy to compute on the other uses. The danger of the tithe is that it can be treated as simply another bill to be paid, and by not having the correct attitude I do not put myself in a position to receive the blessings and advantages God has for me in giving. Another potential danger of tithing is the assumption that once I have tithed, I have fulfilled all my obligations to give. For many Christians, the tithe should be the beginning of their giving, not the limit.

How much should we give? To answer this question, first give yourself to the Lord. Submit yourself to Him. Earnestly seek His will for you concerning giving. Ask Him to help you obey Christ's leading. In my family we are convinced that we should tithe as a minimum and then give over and above the tithe as the Lord prospers or directs us.

Ruth

During Paul's third missionary journey one of his priorities was to take up a collection for the suffering believers in Jerusalem. There are several practical applications from his instructions to the Corinthians concerning this collection. *"On the first day of every week let each one of you put aside and save, as he may prosper, that no collections be made when I come"* (1 Corinthians 16:2).

1. Giving Should Be Periodic

"On the first day of every week. . . ." The Lord understands that we need to give frequently and habitually. Giving only once a year, is a mistake. We need to give regularly to be drawn consistently to Christ.

2. Giving Should Be Personal

". . . let each one of you. . . ." It is the responsibility of every child of God, whether young or old, rich or poor, to give. The advantages of giving are intended for each person, and to be enjoyed, each individual must participate.

"That was the best sermon on giving I've ever heard."

3. Giving Should Be Out of a Private Deposit

". . . put aside and save. . . ." If you experience difficulty in monitoring the money you have decided to give, consider opening a separate checking account (we call ours the "Lord's Account") or setting aside a special "cookie jar" into which you deposit the money you intend to give. Then as needs are brought to your attention, you already will have the money to meet those needs.

4. Giving Should Be a Priority

"Honor the Lord from your wealth, and from the first of all your produce" (Proverbs 3:9). As soon as we receive any income, we should set aside the amount we are going to give. This habit helps us to remember to put Christ first in all we do and defeats the temptation to spend on ourselves the portion we have decided to give.

5. Giving Should Be Premeditated

"Let each one do just as he has purposed in his heart" (2 Corinthians 9:7). Our giving should be done prayerfully, exercising the same care in selecting where we are going to give our money as we do when deciding where to invest our money.

6. Giving Should Be Without Pride

To experience any of the Lord's benefits, your giving cannot be motivated out of a desire to impress people. Matthew 6:1-4 reads, *"Beware of practicing your righteousness before men to be noticed by them; otherwise you have no reward with your Father who is in heaven. When therefore you give alms, do not sound a trumpet before you, as the hypocrites do in the synagogues and in the streets, that they may be honored by men. Truly I say to you, they have their reward in full. But when you give alms, do not let your left hand know what your right hand is doing that your alms may be in secret; and your Father who sees in secret will repay you."*

GIVING NOTES

We are instructed in Scripture to give to three areas. To whom and in what proportion one gives varies with the needs God lays on the heart of each believer.

1. The Church, Christian Workers, and Ministries

Throughout its pages the Bible focuses on maintenance of the ministry. The Old Testament priesthood was to receive specific support: *"And to the sons of Levi, behold, I have given all the tithe in Israel...in return for their service which they perform, the service of the tent of meeting"* (Numbers 18:21). And the New Testament teaching on ministerial support is just as strong. Unfortunately, some have wrongly taught poverty for Christian workers. Thus many believe that those who are in various forms of Christian ministry should be poor. That position is not scriptural.

"Pastors who do their work well should be paid well and should be highly appreciated, especially those who work hard at both preaching and teaching" (1 Timothy 5:17, LB).

How many Christian workers have been driven to distraction from their ministry by inadequate support? God never intended His servants to exist at the level of bare subsistence. As someone has said, "The poor and starving pastor should exist only among poor and starving people."

People ask Bev and me if we give only through our church. In our case, the answer is no. However, we do give a minimum of ten percent of our regular income through our church because this is a tangible expression of our commitment to our church. But we also give to others who are directly impacting us. *"Let the one who is taught the word share all good things with him who teaches"* (Galatians 6:6).

Used by permission of Rob Portlock

"Hi, Pastor. We were just talking about your request for a salary increase."

2. The Family

In our culture we are experiencing a tragic breakdown in this area of giving. Husbands have failed to provide for their wives; parents have neglected their children; and grown sons and daughters have forsaken their elderly parents. Such neglect is solemnly condemned. *"If anyone does not provide for his own, and especially for those of his household, he has denied the faith, and is worse than an unbeliever"* (1 Timothy 5:8). Meeting the needs of your family and relatives is a priority in giving and one in which there should be no compromise.

3. The Poor

In Matthew 25:34-45 we are confronted with one of the most exciting and yet sobering truths in Scripture. Read this passage carefully: *"Then the King will say . . . for I was hungry and you gave Me something to eat; I was thirsty, and you gave Me drink . . . then the righteous will answer Him, saying, Lord, when did we see You hungry, and feed You, or thirsty, and give You drink? . . . the King will answer and say to them, Truly I say to you, to the extent that you did it to one of these brothers of Mine, even the least of them, you did it to Me. Then He will say to those on His left, Depart from Me, accursed ones, into the eternal fire . . . for I was hungry, and you gave Me nothing to eat; I was thirsty, and you gave Me nothing to drink . . . to the extent that you did not do it to one of the least of these, you did not do it to Me."*

In some mysterious way we cannot fully comprehend, Jesus, the Creator of all things, personally identifies Himself with the poor. When we share with the needy we are actually sharing with Jesus Himself. And if that truth is staggering, then the reciprocal is terrifying—when we do not give to the needy, we leave Christ Himself hungry and thirsty.

During Christ's earthly ministry He gave consistently to the poor. It is especially revealing that, during the Last Supper after Jesus told Judas to go and carry out the betrayal, this comment is made: *"Now no one of those reclining at table knew for what purpose He had said this to him. For some were supposing, because Judas had the money box, that Jesus was saying to him, 'Buy things we have need of for the feast'; or else, that he should give something to the poor"* (John 13:28-29).

Giving to the needy was such a natural, consistent part of Jesus' life that the disciples assumed that Jesus was sending Judas either to buy food for their own basic needs or to give to the poor—no other alternative entered their minds. It is small wonder that after Paul meets with the disciples to announce his ministry to the Gentiles that this statement is made: *"They [the disciples] only asked us to remember the poor—the very thing I also was eager to do"* (Galatians 2:10).

Imagine all the theological issues the disciples could have discussed with Paul, but the only one they mentioned was to remember the poor. Now that should tell us something! Three areas of our Christian life are affected by giving or lack of giving to the poor:

■ Prayer

A lack of giving to the poor could be a source of unanswered prayer. *"Is this not the fast which I chose . . . divide your bread with the hungry, and bring the homeless poor into the house . . . then you will call and the Lord will answer"* (Isaiah 58:6-9). *"He who shuts his ear to the cry of the poor will also cry himself and not be answered"* (Proverbs 21:13).

■ Provision

Our provision is partially conditioned upon our giving to the needy. *"He who gives to the poor will never want, but he who shuts his eyes will have many curses"* (Proverbs 28:27).

■ Knowing Jesus Christ intimately

One who does not share with the poor does not know the Lord intimately. *"He pled the cause of the afflicted and the needy; then it was well. Is that not what it means to know Me, declares the Lord"* (Jeremiah 22:16).

Giving to the poor has been discouraged in part because of government programs. I believe it's the church's job and not the government's to meet the needs of the poor. The government often treats the needy impersonally. The

GIVING NOTES

> *"He who gives to the poor will never want, but he who shuts his eyes will have many curses."*
>
> PROVERBS 28:27

church has the potential to be sensitive to the dignity of the poor. We also can develop one-on-one relationships with the poor to meet their immediate physical needs. Then the church can focus on their longer-term physical and spiritual needs—lovingly training and holding accountable those who are capable of becoming self-supporting.

Please consider asking the Lord to bring one needy person into your life; you can do so by praying this prayer: "Father God, by Your grace create in me the desire to share with the poor. Bring a poor person into my life so that I might learn what it really means to give." This will be a significant step in your maturing in your relationship with Christ.

I pray that you and I might be able to echo Job's statement: *"I delivered the poor who cried for help, and the orphan who had no helper . . . I made the widow's heart sing for joy . . . I was eyes to the blind, and feet to the lame. I was a father to the needy, and I investigated the case which I did not know"* (Job 29:12-16).

Secular Charities

Numerous secular charities (such as schools, fraternal orders or organizations that fight diseases) compete vigorously for our gift dollars. Scripture does not address whether or not we should give to these charities. However, my wife and I have decided not to normally support these organizations with our gifts. Our reason is that while many people support secular charities, only those who know the Lord support the ministries of Christ. However, we have occasionally given to secular charities either when the solicitor was a friend we wanted to encourage or influence for Christ, or we sensed the Lord's prompting to give.

Summary

Although the area of giving can be challenging, if done with the proper attitude, it can become one of the most exciting and vibrant parts of your Christian experience.

NEHEMIAH WORKED HARD AND RELIED UPON THE LORD—
*"And I also applied myself to the work on this wall . . . the wall was completed . . .
this work had been accomplished with the help of our God."*

Nehemiah 5:16; 6:15-16

*"Whatever you do, do your work heartily, as for the Lord rather
than for men . . . It is the Lord Christ whom you serve."*
Colossians 3:23-24

WORK

 Scripture to Memorize:

"Whatever you do, do your work heartily, as for the Lord rather than for men; knowing that from the Lord you will receive the reward of the inheritance. It is the Lord Christ whom you serve" (Colossians 3:23-24).

Practical Application: ☐ Complete the Budget Summary practical application.
NOTE: Please give your leader the name of anyone who would be interested in becoming a student in a future group.

DAY ONE

Read the Giving Notes on pages 86 to 94 and answer:

1. From God's perspective it is important to give with the proper attitude. How will this impact your giving?

2. What truth about giving did you learn that proved especially stimulating? In what way?

DAY TWO

Read *Genesis 2:15*.

1. Why is it important to recognize that the Lord created work prior to sin entering the world?

Then read *Genesis 3:17-19.*

2. What was the consequence of sin on work?

Then read *Exodus 20:9* and *2 Thessalonians 3:10-12.*

3. What do these passages say to you about work?

   Exodus 20:9 —

   2 Thessalonians 3:10-12 —

DAY THREE

Read *Genesis 39:2-5; Exodus 35:30-35; Exodus 36:1-2;* **and** *Psalm 75:6-7.*

1. What do each of these verses tell us about the Lord's involvement in our work?

   Genesis 39:2-5 —

   Exodus 35:30-35 —

   Exodus 36:1-2 —

   Psalm 75:6-7 —

2. How do these truths differ from the way most people view work?

3. How will this perspective impact your work?

Read *Ephesians 6:5-9; Colossians 3:22-25;* and *1 Peter 2:18.*

1. What responsibilities do the employer and employee have according to these verses?

    Employee responsibilities:

    Employer responsibilities:

2. For whom do you really work? How will understanding this change your work performance?

Read *Proverbs 6:6-11; Proverbs 18:9;* and *2 Thessalonians 3:7-9* and answer:

1. What does the Lord say about working hard?

   Proverbs 6:6-11—

   Proverbs 18:9—

   2 Thessalonians 3:7-9—

2. Do you work hard? If not, describe what steps you will take to improve your work habits.

Then read *Exodus 34:21.*

3. What does this verse communicate to you about rest?

4. Do you get enough rest?

5. How do you guard against overwork?

Read *Proverbs 31:10-28* **and** *Titus 2:4-5.*

1. What do these passages tell us about women working?

    Proverbs 31:10-28—

    Titus 2:4-5—

2. If you are are woman, how does this apply to your situation?

Then read *2 Corinthians 6:14-18.*

3. How does this concept of "yoking" or "being bound together" apply to partnerships in business and work?

4. Can you give some examples from the Bible of people who retired?

5. Do you think retirement, as it is practiced in our culture, is biblically permissible? Why or why not?

 Please write your prayer requests in your prayer log before coming to class.

 I will take the following action as a result of this week's study:

WORK NOTES

Please do not read these notes until you completed the Work Homework.

Over a 50-year span the average person spends 100,000 hours working. Most of an adult's life is involved in work, but often with the job comes some degree of dissatisfaction. Perhaps no statistic demonstrates this more than job-hopping tendencies. A recent survey found that the average man changes jobs every four and one-half years, the average woman every three years.

Boredom, lack of fulfillment, inadequate wages, and countless other pressures have contributed to this discontentment. Doctors, housewives, salespersons, bluecollar workers, and managers—regardless of the profession— all have experienced similar frustrations. Understanding and applying scriptural principles that relate to work will help you find satisfaction in your job. It will also place you in a position where the Lord can prosper you. We will examine three broad principles of work, explore God's part in work, concentrate on our part in work, and review several practical work issues.

BIBLICAL PERSPECTIVE OF WORK

A job is not merely a task designed to earn money; it is also intended to produce godly character in the life of the worker.

Even before sin entered the human race, God instituted work. *"The Lord God took the man and put him into the garden of Eden to cultivate it and keep it"* (Genesis 2:15). The very first thing the Lord did with Adam was to put him to work. Despite what many believe, work was initiated for our benefit in the sinless environment of the garden of Eden. Work is not a result of the curse!

After the fall, work was made more difficult. *"Cursed is the ground because of you; in toil you shall eat of it all the days of your life. Both thorns and thistles it shall grow for you; and you shall eat the plants of the field; by the sweat of your face you shall eat bread"* (Genesis 3:17-19).

Work is so important that in Exodus 34:21 God gives this command: *"You shall work six days."* In the New Testament we discover that Paul is just as direct. *"If anyone will not work, neither let him eat"* (2 Thessalonians 3:10). Examine the verse carefully. It says, *"If anyone **will** not work."* It did not say, *"If anyone **cannot** work."* This principle does not apply to those who are physically or mentally unable to work. It is for those who are able but choose not to work.

A close friend has a sister in her mid-thirties whose parents have always supported her. She has never had to face the responsibilities and hardships involved in a job. As a consequence, her character has not been properly developed. She is hopelessly immature in many areas of her life.

One of the primary purposes of work is to develop character. While the carpenter is building a house, the house is also building the carpenter. His skill, diligence, manual dexterity, and judgment are refined. A job is not merely a task designed to earn money; it's also intended to produce godly character in the life of the worker.

ALL HONEST PROFESSIONS ARE HONORABLE

According to Scripture there is dignity in all types of work. Scripture does not elevate any honest profession above another. A wide variety of vocations are represented in the Bible. David was a shepherd and a king. Luke was a doctor. Lydia was a retailer who sold purple fabric. Daniel was a government worker. Paul was a tentmaker, and Amos was a fig-picker.

If God can use a fig-picker, he can certainly use us in our jobs! And finally, the Lord Jesus was a carpenter.

In God's economy there is equal dignity in the labor of the automobile mechanic and the president of General Motors, in the labor of the pastor and a secretary serving the church.

Lydia

GOD'S PART IN WORK

Scripture reveals three responsibilities the Lord has in work.

1. God Gives Job Skills

Exodus 36:1 illustrates this truth: *"And every skillful person in whom the Lord has put skill and understanding to know how to perform all the work."* God has given each of us unique skills. People have a wide variety of abilities, manual skills, and intellectual capacities. It is not a matter of one person being better than another; it is simply a matter of having received different abilities.

2. God Gives Success

The life of Joseph is a perfect example of God helping a person to succeed. *"The Lord was with Joseph, so he became a successful man . . . his master saw that the Lord was with him and how the Lord caused all that he did to prosper in his hand"* (*Genesis 39:2-3*). As we have seen, you and I have certain responsibilities, but we need to recognize that it is ultimately God who gives us success.

3. God Controls Promotion

Psalm 75:6-7 reads, *"For promotion and power come from nowhere on earth, but only from God"* (LB). As much as it may surprise you, your boss is not the one who controls whether or not you will be promoted. Understanding this truth should have a tremendous impact on the way we perform as employees. Most people find this hard to believe. Our culture leaves God out of work. People believe they alone control their success and promotions and are solely responsible for their job skills. However, those with a biblical understanding will approach work with an entirely different frame of reference.

One of the major reasons people experience stress and frustration in their jobs is because they don't understand God's part in work. Stop reading for a few minutes. Think about God's part—He gives you your skills and controls success and promotion. How should this perspective impact you and your job?

WORK NOTES

Scripture reveals we actually are serving the Lord in our work and not people. *"Whatever you do, do your work heartily, as for the Lord rather than for men; knowing that from the Lord you will receive the reward of the inheritance. It is the Lord Christ whom you serve"* (Colossians 3:23-24). Recognizing that we are actually working for the Lord has profound implications.

Consider your attitude toward work. If you could see the person of Jesus Christ as your boss, would you try to be more faithful in your job? The most important question you need to answer every day as you begin your work is this: "For whom do I work?" You work for Christ.

WORK HARD

"Whatever your hand finds to do, verily do it with all your might" (Ecclesiastes 9:10). *"The precious possession of a man is diligence"* (Proverbs 12:27). In Scripture hard work and diligence are encouraged while laziness is repeatedly condemned: *"He who is slack in his work is brother to him who destroys"* (Proverbs 18:9).

Paul's life was an example of hard work. *"With labor and hardship we kept working night and day so that we might not be a burden to any of you . . . in order to offer ourselves as a model for you, that you might follow our example"* (2 Thessalonians 3:8-9).

"SO MR. PHELPS, WHAT MAKES YOU THINK THAT YOU'RE EXPERIENCING BURNOUT?"

Your work should be at such a level that people will never equate laziness with God. Nothing less than hard work and the pursuit of excellence pleases the Lord. We are not required to be "superworkers" who never make mistakes. Rather, the Lord expects us to do the best we possibly can.

BUT DO NOT OVERWORK!

Hard work, however, must be balanced by the other priorities of life. If your job demands so much of your time and energy that you neglect your relationship with Christ or your family, then you are working too hard. You should determine whether the job is too demanding, or your work habits need changing. If you tend to be a "workaholic," take extra precautions to guard against forsaking the other priorities of life.

Exodus 34:21 reads, *"You shall work six days, but on the seventh day you shall rest; even during plowing time and harvest you shall rest."* I believe this Old Testament principle of resting one day out of seven has application for us today. This has been difficult for me, particularly during times of "plowing or harvesting" when a project deadline is approaching or I am under financial pressure.

Rest can become an issue of faith. Is the Lord able to make our six days of work more productive than seven days? Yes! The Lord instituted this weekly rest for our physical, mental, and spiritual health. Study the diagram below to understand the balance God wants in our lives.

A Balanced life with Contentment

EMPLOYER'S RESPONSIBILITIES

The godly employer performs a balancing act. The employer is to love, serve, and encourage the employee. Yet the employer also is responsible to lead employees and to hold them accountable for the completion of their assigned tasks. Let's examine several principles that should govern an employer's conduct.

1. Serve Your Employees

The basis for biblical leadership is servanthood: *"Whoever wishes to become great among you shall be your servant"* (Matthew 20:26). Too often employers have concentrated on producing a profit at the expense of their personnel. However, the Bible directs the employer to balance efforts to make a profit with an unselfish concern for employees. Employees are to be treated fairly and with genuine dignity. *"Masters* [employers], *grant your slaves* [employees] *justice and fairness, knowing that you too have a Master in heaven"* (Colossians 4:1).

Employers should attempt to be creative as they serve their employees. For example, they should consider investing time and money to educate and upgrade their employees' job skills. This will help employees to grow in their capabilities and thus earn more.

2. Be a Good Communicator

The Genesis account of building the tower of Babel supports the importance of good communication. At that time everyone spoke the same language and adopted a common goal. The Lord makes this remarkable observation, *"If as one people speaking the same language they have begun to do this, then nothing they plan to do will be impossible for them"* (Genesis 11:6, NIV).

When a group of people are committed to accomplishing a particular task, and there is good communication, then *"nothing they plan to do will be impossible for them"*—as long as it's within the will of God. Since building the tower was not what the Lord wanted, He stopped construction. He disrupted their ability to communicate, which was the foundation for successfully completing the tower. *"Come, let Us go down and confuse their language so they will not understand each other"* (Genesis 11:7, NIV).

It's especially important to listen to employee complaints. *"If I have despised the claim of my . . . [employees] when they filed a complaint against me, what then could I do when God arises, and when He calls me to account, what will I answer Him?"* (Job 31:13-15). A sensitive, listening ear is a tangible expression that you care about the other person. When a complaint is legitimate, the employer should take appropriate steps to solve the problem.

3. Hold Employees Accountable

The employer is responsible for the employees knowing what is expected on the job. The employer should regularly evaluate employee performance and communicate this to them. If an employee is not performing satisfactorily and is unable or unwilling to change, it may necessitate a personnel change.

4. Pay Your Employees a Fair Wage Promptly.

Employers are warned to pay a fair wage. "[The Lord will judge] *those who oppress the wage earner in his wages*" (Malachi 3:5). They also are commanded to pay wages promptly when due. *"You shall not oppress a hired [employee] . . . give him his wages on his day before the sun sets . . . so that he may not cry against you to the Lord and it become sin in you"* (Deuteronomy 24:14-15).

5. Pray for Godly Employees

The Lord may choose to bless an employer for having a godly employee. Scripture gives two examples of this. First of all, *"But Laban said to him [Jacob], 'If now it pleases you, stay with me; I have divined that the Lord has blessed me on your account"* (Genesis 30:27). Secondly, *"So Joseph found favor in his [Potiphar's] sight . . . and it came about that from the time he made him [Joseph] overseer in his house, and over all that he owned, the Lord blessed the Egyptian's house on account of Joseph; thus the Lord's blessing was upon all that he owned, in the house and in the field"* (Genesis 39:4-5).

Because of this principle I always wanted to employ Raymond who was an especially godly construction worker on the job. He was strong and did the work of two men. But far more important than his productivity, was Raymond's influence over the project. There was less profanity and pilferage, and he was a tremendous model to all who labored. This principle is not a command, but I believe the wise employer will pray for the Lord to bring a "Raymond" to his or her company.

EMPLOYEE'S RESPONSIBILITIES

We can identify the six major responsibilities of the godly employee by examining the well-known story of Daniel in the lion's den. In Daniel chapter 6 we are told that Darius, the king of Babylon, appointed 120 men to administer the government, and three men, one of whom was Daniel, to supervise these administrators. King Darius decided to promote Daniel to govern the entire kingdom. Daniel's fellow employees then looked for a way to remove him from his job. After this failed they asked King Darius, to enact a law requiring everyone in the kingdom to worship only the king

A sensitive, listening ear is a tangible expression that you care about the other person. When a complaint is legitimate, the employer should take appropriate steps to solve the problem.

or die in the lion's den. Daniel was thrown to the lions after refusing to stop worshipping the living God. The Lord then rescued Daniel by sending His angel to shut the lions' mouths. The six characteristics of a godly employee are:

1. Absolute Honesty

Daniel 6:4 tells us that Daniel's fellow employees could find no grounds for accusation against him in regard to his job, and there was *"no evidence of corruption"* in Daniel's work. He was absolutely honest. We studied the importance of honesty earlier.

2. Faithfulness

We discover the second element of the godly employee in Daniel 6:4: *"He was faithful."* The godly employee needs to establish the goal of being faithful and excellent in work, then to work hard to attain that goal.

3. Prayerfulness

The godly employee is a person of prayer. *"Now when Daniel knew that the document was signed* [restricting worship to the king alone] *. . . he continued kneeling on his knees three times a day, praying and giving thanks before his God, as he had been doing previously"* (Daniel 6:10). Daniel's job was that of governing the most powerful country of his day. Few of us will ever be faced with the magnitude of his responsibilities and the demands upon his time. Yet he knew the importance and priority of prayer. If you are not praying consistently, your work is suffering.

4. Honors Employer

"Daniel spoke to the king, 'O king live forever!'" (Daniel 6:21). What a remarkable response from Daniel. The king, his employer, had been tricked into sentencing Daniel to the lion's den. But Daniel's reaction was to honor his boss. Think how natural it would have been to say something like, "You dummy! The God who sent His angel to shut the lion's mouth is now going to punish you!" Instead, he honored his boss.

The godly employee always honors his superior. 1 Peter 2:18 reads, *"Servants* [employees] *be submissive to your masters* [employer] *with all respect, not only to those who are good and gentle, but also to those who are unreasonable."* One way to honor your employer is to never participate in gossip behind your employer's back, even if he or she is not an ideal person.

5. Honors Fellow Employees

People may damage your reputation to secure a promotion over you or even have you terminated from your job. They tried to murder Daniel. Despite this, there is no evidence that Daniel did anything but honor his fellow employees. Never slander a fellow employee behind his back. *"Do not slander a slave* [employee] *to his master* [employer], *lest he curse you and you be found guilty"* (Proverbs 30:10).

The godly person should avoid office politics and manipulation to secure a promotion. Your superior does not control your promotion! The Lord Himself makes that determination. We can be content in our jobs by striving for faithfulness, honoring superiors, and encouraging our fellow employees. Having done this, we can rest knowing that Christ will promote us if and when He chooses.

6. Verbalizes Faith

King Darius would never have known about the living God if Daniel had not communicated his faith verbally at appropriate moments while at work, *"The king spoke and said to Daniel, 'Daniel, servant of the living God, has your God, whom you constantly serve, been able to deliver you from the lions?'"* (Daniel 6:20). King Darius would not have been as powerfully influenced by Daniel sharing his faith if he had not observed him fulfilling his work responsibilities with honesty and faithfulness. Listen to the words of Darius: *"I make a decree that in all the dominion of my kingdom men are to fear and tremble before the God of Daniel; for He is the living God and enduring forever, and His kingdom is one which will not be destroyed, and His dominion will be forever"* (Daniel 6:26).

Daniel influenced his employer, one of the most powerful people in the world, to believe in the only true and living God. You have that same opportunity in your own God-given sphere of work. Let me say this another way. A job well done earns you the right to tell others with whom you work about the reality of Christ. As we view our work from God's perspective, dissatisfaction will turn to contentment from a job well done, and drudgery will become excitement over the prospect of introducing others to the Savior.

OTHER WORK ISSUES

RETIREMENT

The dictionary defines retirement as: "withdrawal from an occupation or business, to give up or retreat from an active life." The goal of retirement is deeply ingrained in our culture. Many people retire at an arbitrary, predetermined age and cease all labor in the pursuit of a life filled with leisure.

Scripture gives no examples of people retiring and gives only one direct reference to retirement which is found in Numbers 8:24-26. The instruction there applied exclusively to the Levites who worked on the tabernacle. As long as one is physically and mentally capable, there is no scriptural basis for a person retiring and becoming unproductive. The concept of putting an older but able person "out to pasture" is unbiblical. Age is no obstacle in finishing the work the Lord has for you to accomplish. He will provide you with the necessary vigor and stamina. For example, Moses was 80 years old when he began his 40-year adventure leading the children of Israel.

"I can't retire! I haven't paid off my student loan yet."

Scripture does imply that the type or the intensity of work may change as we grow older—a shifting of the gears to a less demanding pace to become more of an "elder seated at the gate." During this season of life we can use the experience and wisdom gained over a lifetime. If we have sufficient income to meet our needs apart from our job, we may choose to leave the job to invest more time in serving others in whatever capacity the Lord directs.

AMBITION

Scripture does not condemn ambition. Paul was ambitious. *"We have as our ambition . . . to be pleasing to Him"* (2 Corinthians 5:9). What is strongly denounced is selfish ambition. The Lord *"will render to every man according to his deeds . . . to those who are selfishly ambitious . . . wrath and indignation"* (Romans 2:6,8). *"But if you have . . . selfish ambition in your heart, do not be arrogant and so lie against the truth. This wisdom is not that which comes down from above, but is earthly, natural, demonic. For where . . . selfish ambition exists, there is disorder and every evil thing"* (James 3:14-16).

The Bible is not the enemy of ambition, only of the wrong type of ambition. Our ambition should not be motivated out of an egotistical desire. *"But you, are you seeking great things for yourself? Do not seek them"* (Jeremiah 45:5). The motivation for our ambition should be to please Christ. We should have a burning desire to become an increasingly faithful steward in using the possessions and skills entrusted to us. In our work we should try to please the Lord by discharging our job responsibilities to the best of our ability.

CALLING

Each of us has a specific calling or purpose which the Lord intends for us. The root meaning of the word "vocation" has to do with a call to a particular task. Ephesians 2:10 reads, *"For we are His workmanship, created in Christ Jesus for good works, which God prepared beforehand, that we should walk in them."* Study this passage carefully. *"We are His workmanship."* The Amplified Bible says, *"We are His handiwork."* Each of us has been created uniquely and given special physical, emotional, and mental characteristics and abilities. You probably have heard the expression, "After the Lord made you, He threw away the mold!" It's true! You are gifted uniquely. No one in all of history—past, present or future—is like you.

The passage continues, *"created in Christ Jesus for good works, which God prepared beforehand that we should walk in them."* The Lord created each of us for a particular job, and He endowed us with the proper skills, aptitudes, and desires to accomplish this work. This calling may be full-time Christian service or a secular job. Often people struggle with whether God wants them to continue in their work once they commit their lives to Christ. Many feel they are not serving Christ in a significant way if they remain at their job. Nothing could be further from the truth. The key is for each person to determine God's call for his or her life.

In his book, *God Owns My Business*, Stanley Tamm writes, "Although

I believe in the application of good principles in business, I place far more confidence in the conviction that I have a call from God. I am convinced that His purpose for me is in the business world. My business is my pulpit." To those who earn a living through secular pursuits, it is a great comfort to know that the "call" of holy vocation carries over into all walks of life. God strategically places His children everywhere!

Each of us has been created uniquely and given special physical, emotional, and mental characteristics and abilities.

PARTNERSHIPS

Scripture clearly discourages business partnerships with those who do not know Christ. In 2 Corinthians 6:14-17 it reads, *"Do not be bound together* [unequally yoked] *with unbelievers; for what partnership have righteousness and lawlessness, or what fellowship has light with darkness? Or what harmony has Christ with Belial, or what has a believer in common with an unbeliever? Or what agreement has the temple of God with idols? For we are the temple of the living God; just as God said, 'I will dwell in them and walk among them; and I will be their God, and they shall be My people. Therefore, come out from their midst and be separate, says the Lord.'"* Many have violated this principle and have suffered financially.

In my opinion, we should also be careful before entering into a partnership even with another Christian. I would consider only a few people as potential partners. These are people I have known well for years. I have observed their commitment to the Lord, I know their strengths and weaknesses, and I have seen them handle money faithfully. **Do not rush into a partnership!** Prayerfully evaluate it.

FRANK'S NOT WHAT YOU'D CALL A MORNING PERSON.

Before forming a partnership, reduce your understandings into writing. Develop this agreement with your future partner, and be sure to include a way to dissolve the partnership. If you are not able to agree in writing, do not become partners.

PROCRASTINATION

A procrastinator is someone who, because of laziness or fear, has a habit of putting things off until later. Often this habit can develop into a serious character flaw.

The Bible has many examples of godly people who were not procrastinators, and one of my favorite examples is Boaz. Naomi, the mother-in-law of Ruth, made this comment about Ruth's future husband, Boaz: *"Wait, my daughter, until you know how the matter turns out; for the man will not rest until he has settled it today"* (Ruth 3:18). Boaz had the reputation of a person who acted promptly.

Here are some practical suggestions to help overcome procrastination: (1) List the things you need to do each day. (2) Prayerfully review the list and prioritize it according to the tasks you need to accomplish first. (3) Finish the first task on your list before starting the second. Often that first task is the most difficult or the one you fear the most. (4) Ask the Lord to give you courage, remembering Philippians 4:13, *"I can do all things through Him who strengthens me."*

SHOULD WIVES WORK OUTSIDE THE HOME?

For many reasons, women are becoming involved in jobs of all kinds. Married women work to provide additional income for their families, to express their creativity, or because they enjoy their job. Widows and divorcees often must work to provide for the basic needs of their families. A Stanford University study found that wives who work outside the home carry a particularly heavy load of 70 to 80 hours a week. This includes the responsibilities of their jobs and their household work.

In my opinion, during the children's early formative years, if possible, it is preferable for the mother to be home when the children are home. Titus 2:4-5 reads, *"Encourage the young women to love their husbands, to love their children, to be sensible, pure, workers at home."* It is ideal to limit working outside the home to those times when children are not at home unless the family finances depend upon her income. As the children mature, a mother will have increased freedom to pursue outside work.

Proverbs 31:10-31 reads, *"An excellent wife . . . does him [her husband] good and not evil all the days of her life. She looks for wool and flax, and works with her hands . . . she brings her food from afar. She rises also while it is still night, and gives food to her household. . . . She considers a field and buys it; from her earnings she plants a vineyard. . . . She stretches out her hands to the distaff, and her hands grasp the spindle. She extends her hand to the poor. . . . She makes coverings for herself; her clothing is fine linen and purple. Her husband is known in the gates, when he sits among the elders of the land. She makes linen garments and sells them, and supplies belts to the tradesmen. . . . She looks well to the ways of her household, and does not eat the bread of idleness."*

Proverbs 31 paints a picture of the working wife living a balanced life with the thrust of her activity toward the home. Some women are gifted as homemakers, and there is no more important task than raising godly children. However, other women must work to earn income or they have the skill and desire to work outside the home. Either way, it is a decision that the husband and wife should make prayerfully and with full agreement.

If a wife works to earn additional income for her family, it is important to analyze exactly what income, after taxes and expenses, her work contributes. In the "Example 1" column of the worksheet on the next page, the following assumptions have been made: working 40 hours a week and earning $9 per hour; giving 10 percent of the gross income; federal income tax of 25 percent (a wife's income is added to a husband's and taxed at the higher rate); state income tax of 5 percent; Social security tax of 7.5 percent; ten trips of five miles at a cost of 25 cents a mile; lunch, snacks, and coffee breaks of $15; eating out more often and using convenience foods add $35 a week to the budget; $20 for extra clothing and cleaning is needed; $5 more is spent for grooming; extra child care of $45 a week. In the "Example 2" column we assume she earns $25 an hour, with all other assumptions remaining the same.

These assumptions are for illustration only, and may not represent your situation. Complete the exercise on the following page to determine the actual net income for the family.

Couples often are surprised to learn that the income earned by a working wife is not as much as they had expected.

Couples often are surprised to learn that the income earned by a working wife is not as much as they had expected. Some have actually produced more net income (after reducing work related expenses) when they decided to work in some creative way while staying at home. Of course, the financial benefits are not the only factors to evaluate. Consideration should also be given to the physical and emotional demands of working and how they affect a family.

Income and spending	Example 1	Example 2	Your Situation
Wife's gross yearly income:	$ 18,720.00	$ 52,000.00	
Wife's gross weekly income:	$ 360.00	$ 1,000.00	
Wife's expenses:			
Giving	$ 36.00	$ 100.00	
Federal income tax	$ 90.00	$ 250.00	
State income tax	$ 18.00	$ 50.00	
Social security tax	$ 27.00	$ 75.00	
Transportation	$ 15.00	$ 15.00	
Lunch/snacks/coffee breaks	$ 15.00	$ 15.00	
Restaurants/convenience food	$ 35.00	$ 35.00	
Extra clothing/cleaning	$ 20.00	$ 20.00	
Personal grooming	$ 5.00	$ 5.00	
Child care	$ 45.00	$ 45.00	
TOTAL EXPENSES:	$ 306.00	$ 610.00	
NET ADDITIONAL FAMILY INCOME:	$ 54.00	$ 390.00	
NET INCOME PER HOUR:	$ 1.35	$ 9.75	

JOSEPH —
GATHERED DURING THE 7 YEARS OF PLENTY
TO PROVIDE FOR THE 7 YEARS OF FAMINE

"Steady plodding brings prosperity."
Proverbs 21:5, LB

INVESTING

 Scripture to Memorize:

"The wise man saves for the future, but the foolish man spends whatever he gets" (Proverbs 21:20, LB) and *"Steady plodding brings prosperity; hasty speculation brings poverty"* (Proverbs 21:5, LB).

Practical Application: □ Complete the "Organizing Your Estate" practical application and continue your budget. □ Remember to secure a current will if you do not yet have one.

DAY ONE

Read the Work Notes on pages 101 to 111 and answer:

1. What in the notes proved especially stimulating or challenging? How will this impact you?

2. Do you usually recognize you are working for the Lord? If not, what can you do to be more aware that you work for the Lord?

Read *Genesis 41:34-36; Proverbs 21:20;* **and** *Proverbs 30:24-25* **and answer:**

1. What do these passages communicate to you about savings?

    Genesis 41:34-36 —

    Proverbs 21:20 —

    Proverbs 30:24-25 —

2. If you are not yet saving, how do you propose to begin?

Read *Luke 12:16-21, 34.*

3. Why did the Lord call the rich man a fool?

4. According to this parable, why do you think it is scripturally permissible to save only when you are also giving?

Read *1 Timothy 5:8* and answer:

1. What is a scripturally acceptable goal for saving?

Then read *1 Timothy 6:9*.

2. What is a scripturally unacceptable reason for saving?

Then read *1 Timothy 6:10*.

3. According to this verse, why is it wrong to want to get rich (refer to *1 Timothy 6:9)?* Do you have the desire to get rich?

Then read *1 Timothy 6:11*.

4. What should you do if you have the desire to get rich?

Read *Proverbs 21:5; Proverbs 24:27; Proverbs 27:23-24; Ecclesiastes 3:1; Ecclesiastes 11:2;* **and** *Isaiah 48:17-18.*

1. What investment principle(s) can you learn from each of these verses, and how will you apply each principle to your life?

   Proverbs 21:5—

   Proverbs 24:27—

   Proverbs 27:23-24—

   Ecclesiastes 3:1—

   Ecclesiastes 11:2—

   Isaiah 48:17-18—

INVESTING

Read *Genesis 24:35-36; Proverbs 13:22;* **and** *2 Corinthians 12:14.*

1. Should parents attempt to leave a material inheritance to their children?

2. How are you going to implement this principle?

Then read *Proverbs 20:21* **and** *Galatians 4:1-2.*

3. What caution should a parent exercise?

  Proverbs 20:21—

  Galatians 4:1-2—

Gambling is defined as: playing games of chance for money, betting, taking great risks, and speculating. Some of today's most common forms of gambling are casino wagering, betting on sporting events, horse and dog races, and state-run lotteries.

1. What are some of the motivations that cause people to gamble?

2. Do these motives please the Lord? Why?

Read *Proverbs 28:20* **and** *Proverbs 28:22.*

3. According to these passages, why do you think a godly person should not gamble (play lotteries, bet on sporting events, etc.)?

4. How does gambling contradict the scriptural principles of working diligently and being a faithful steward of the Lord's possessions?

Please write your prayer requests in your prayer log before coming to class.

I will take the following action as a result of this week's study:

INVESTING NOTES

Please do not read these notes until you completed the Investing Homework.

We must answer a question before we can say investing is scripturally legitimate. Is money evil? The answer to that is a resounding NO! It is morally neutral. Money can be used for good or evil; for supporting missionaries and building hospitals, or for financing hard drugs and pornography. The Bible never condemns money itself, only the misuse of or the wrong attitude toward it.

The Bible never condemns money itself, only the misuse of or the wrong attitude toward it.

LEGITIMATE INVESTING

Examine 1 Timothy 6:10 carefully: *"The love of money is a root of all sorts of evil."* Not the money itself, but the wrong attitude toward money is the root of much evil. Particularly in the Old Testament, many of the most godly people were also among the more wealthy people of the day. Job, Abraham, and David were all wealthy, and yet they did not allow wealth to interfere with their relationship with the Lord.

It seems difficult to explain Matthew 6:19-21, which seems to legislate against saving and investing: *"Do not lay up for yourselves treasures upon earth, where moth and rust destroy, and where thieves break in and steal; but lay up for yourselves treasures in heaven . . . for where your treasure is, there will your heart be also."*

Jesus clarifies this issue in the parable of a rich man who laid up treasures for himself. *"The land of a certain rich man was very productive. And he began reasoning to himself, saying, 'What shall I do, since I have no place to store my crops?' And he said, 'This is what I will do: I will tear down my barns and build larger ones, and there I will store all my grain and my goods. And I will say to my soul, "Soul, you have many goods laid up for many years to come; take your ease, eat, drink and be merry." But God said to him, 'You fool! This very night your soul is required of you; and now who will own what you have prepared?' So is the man who lays up treasures for himself and is not rich toward God . . . for where your treasure is, there will your heart be also"* (Luke 12:16-21, 34).

The key word in this parable is "all." Jesus called the rich man a fool because he saved **all** of his goods. He stored them up for his own use. He did not balance his saving with generous giving. It is legitimate to save and invest only when we also are giving to the Lord. Why? *"Where your treasure is, there will your heart be also"* (Matthew 6:21). If we concentrate solely on saving and investing, our focus and affection will gravitate to those possessions. But if we balance our saving and investing by giving generously to the Lord, we can still love Christ first with all our heart.

Before you develop your individual investment strategy, you must establish investment goals. I believe three goals are acceptable for investing:

1. To Provide for Your Family

In 1 Timothy 5:8 it reads, *"If anyone does not provide for his own, and especially for those of his household, he has denied the faith and is worse than an unbeliever."* This principle extends to providing for your needs in old age and leaving an inheritance to your children.

2. To Become Free Financially to Serve the Lord

One objective of saving is to diminish our dependence on a salary to meet our needs. This affords us the freedom to invest more volunteer time in ministry if this is God's plan for us. The more income my savings and investments produce, the less I am dependent on income from my work. Some have saved enough to be free one day a week, and others are in a position to be a full-time volunteer without the need to earn a salary.

I'm sorry I took so long, Sir, but those teeny-weeny accounts are so hard to find!

Tom Wilson

3. To Operate Your Business

I believe it is proper to save and invest enough capital to operate a business without going into debt. The amount of capital may vary substantially. It depends on the personnel and inventory requirements of each business.

HOW MUCH IS ENOUGH?

When a runner breaks the tape at the finish line, he or she rarely continues running. However, many people who already have achieved the three acceptable investment goals continue accumulating. I believe that each of us should establish a maximum amount we are going to accumulate, and once we have "finished this race," we should give away the portion of our income that we were saving. This "finish line" on accumulation protects us against the dangers of hoarding.

UNACCEPTABLE INVESTMENT GOALS

One investment goal—the desire to become rich—is strictly prohibited. First Timothy 6:9 states, *"But those who want to get rich fall into temptation and a snare and many foolish and harmful desires which plunge men into ruin and destruction."* Study this carefully. It does not say most of those who want to get rich; it says those who want to get rich. **Everyone** who wants to get rich will *"fall into temptation and a snare and many foolish and harmful desires which plunge men into ruin and destruction."*

Nothing is wrong with becoming wealthy if it is a by-product of being a faithful steward.

For most of my life I wanted to become rich—not just a little rich—filthy rich! So dealing with the biblical prohibition against this attitude has been painful. Sometimes, even now, I vacillate between wanting to get rich and wanting to be a faithful steward. When I want to get rich, I am self-centered. My motivations for wanting to get rich may vary—pride, greed, or an unhealthy compulsion to prepare for survival in an uncertain economic future. But when I desire to be a faithful steward, I am Christ-centered in my thoughts and attitudes. My actions are then motivated by a pure heart. I am serving Christ and growing closer to Him.

The next verse, 1 Timothy 6:10, reveals another reason our Lord warns us not to want to get rich: *"For the love of money is a root of all sorts of evil, and some by longing for it have wandered away from the faith, and pierced themselves with many a pang."* When we want to get rich, Scripture tells us that we are loving money. And in Matthew 6:24 we read, *"No one can serve two masters; for either he will hate the one and love the other, or he will hold to one and despise the other. You cannot serve God and mammon [money]."*

When we want to get rich, we are actually loving money and hating God. We are holding to money and despising God. We are serving money, and we are not serving the living God. First Timothy 6:10 ends by saying, *"Some by longing for riches have wandered away from the faith and pierced themselves with many a pang."* I have witnessed firsthand the truth of this scripture. I admired and respected the man who led me to Christ. However, he became consumed by a desire to get rich. He divorced his wife and abandoned his four young sons. He denied Christ repeatedly and wandered away from the faith. Wanting to get rich, which is the love of money, is a devastating spiritual condition.

Understand me clearly. I am not saying it is wrong to become rich. In fact, I rejoice seeing God enable a man or woman to prosper who has been ambitious enough to be a faithful steward. **Nothing is wrong with becoming wealthy if it is a by-product of being a faithful steward.**

SPLIT AND SUBMIT

How can we overcome the temptation to get rich? By remembering to split and submit! In the next verse, 1 Timothy 6:11, Paul counsels Timothy to *"flee from these things [the desire to get rich], you man of God; and pursue righteousness, godliness, faith, love, perseverance and gentleness."* When you become aware of your desire to become rich, you must flee (split) from that temptation and replace it with the pursuit of godliness. Analyze what triggers your desire. A pattern may emerge. I discovered an unrecognized habit of dreaming about becoming rich whenever I would take a long automobile trip alone. I started to break the habit by listening to Christian tapes to help me concentrate on the Lord while I'm driving.

Secondly, submit. The ultimate way of escape is found in submitting to Jesus as Lord. We can do this in perfect confidence because Jesus overcame a massive temptation to become incredibly rich. After Christ fasted 40 days in the wilderness, the devil tempted Him three times. The final temptation is recorded in Luke 4:5-7: *"And he* [the devil] *led Him* [Jesus] *up and showed Him all the kingdoms of the world in a moment of time. And the devil said to Him, 'I will give You all this domain and its glory if You worship me.'"*

Jesus was exposed to all the kingdoms of the world in a moment of time. But because He was submitted entirely to the Father and empowered by the same Holy Spirit who lives in us, He was able to resist that temptation.

I am of the opinion that our heavenly Father usually will not allow His children to prosper when they are motivated to get rich. Wanting to get rich—loving money—closely parallels greed. And *"greed . . . amounts to idolatry"* (Colossians 3:5). The Father watches jealously over His children to insure that we will not be drawn away from loving Him with all of our hearts.

SAVING

Once we have established our investment goals, the first step is saving. Unfortunately, most people are not consistent savers. The average person in our country is three weeks away from bankruptcy. He has little or no money saved, regular obligations to support a relatively high lifestyle, significant credit obligations, and a total dependence on next week's paycheck to keep the budget afloat.

Scripture encourages us to save. *"The wise man saves for the future, but the foolish man spends whatever he gets"* (Proverbs 21:20, LB). The ant is commended for saving for a future need. *"Four things on earth are small, yet they are extremely wise; ants are creatures of little strength, yet they store up their food in the summer"* (Proverbs 30:24-25, NIV). Savings is the opposite of being in debt. Saving is making **provision** for tomorrow, while debt is **presumption** upon tomorrow.

There are several arguments against saving. The government's tax structure rewards indebtedness because some interest is tax deductible, and penalizes saving because most earned interest is taxable. Nevertheless, this does not alter our obligation to be faithful stewards who save. Many people have an aversion to saving because inflation reduces the purchasing power of their savings. However, unless you first save you will never accumulate sufficient reserves to make the kind of investments that are designed to keep pace with inflation.

I call saving the "Joseph principle" because saving requires self-denial. Joseph saved during seven years of plenty to survive during seven years of famine. Saving is denying an expenditure today so that you will have something to spend in the future. One of the major reasons most people are poor savers is that the average person does not practice self-denial. When we want something, we want it now!

HOW TO SAVE AND HOW MUCH TO SAVE
The most effective way to save is to do it whenever you receive income. The first check you write should be giving to the Lord and the second check to your

The average person in our country is three weeks away from bankruptcy. He has little or no money saved, regular fixed obligations to support a relatively high lifestyle, significant monthly credit obligations, and a total dependence on next week's paycheck to keep the budget afloat.

savings. An automatic payroll deduction can help insure that a portion of your income is saved regularly. Some commit income from tax refunds or bonuses to be saved. Recognize this: If you immediately save a portion of your income each time you are paid, you will save more. The Bible does not teach a percentage to be saved. We recommend establishing a goal of saving 10 percent of your income. This may not be possible initially, but begin the habit of saving—even if only a dollar a month.

THERE ARE TWO TYPES OF SAVINGS:

1. Long-term Savings
Long-term savings are intended to fund long-term needs and goals, such as retirement income and inheritances. Pensions and retirement accounts fall into this category. Except for extreme financial emergencies, these savings should not be used for any purpose. They could be called "never-to-spend savings." Spending these savings often results in tax consequences, and the savings are rarely replenished once they are spent.

2. Short-term Savings
Short-term savings should be in an account that is readily accessible. They may include interest bearing accounts, mutual funds, and so forth. These are designed to be used for future planned spending—acquiring or replacing items such as appliances or cars and making major home repairs. Short-term savings should also be set aside for emergencies—an illness, loss of job, or other interruption of income. Financial experts recommend you save the equivalent of three to six months of income for such a fund.

INVESTING

People place some of their savings in investments in the hope of receiving an income or growth in value. **The purpose of this** Crown Financial Ministries **Study is not to recommend any specific investments. No one is authorized to use affiliation with** Crown **to promote the sale of any investments or financial services.** Our objective is to draw attention to the scriptural framework for savings and investing. Visit Crown's web site for more detailed information on investing.

STEADY PLODDING
"Steady plodding brings prosperity, hasty speculation brings poverty" (Proverbs 21:5, LB). The original Hebrew words for *"steady plodding"* picture a person filling a large barrel one handful at a time. Little by little the barrel is filled to overflowing. **The fundamental principle you need to practice to become a successful investor is to spend less than you earn. Then save and invest the difference over a long period of time.**

The fundamental principle you need to practice to become a successful investor is to spend less than you earn. Then save and invest the difference over a long period of time.

Examine various investments. Almost all of them are well suited for "steady plodding." Your home mortgage is paid off after years of steady payments. Savings grow because of compounding interest and your business can increase steadily in value through the years as you develop its potential.

UNDERSTANDING COMPOUND INTEREST

Wealthy Baron Rothschild was once asked if he had seen the seven wonders of the world. He responded, "No, but I do know the eighth wonder of the world—compound interest." Understanding how compounding works is crucial. There are three variables in compounding—the amount you save, the percentage rate you earn, and the length of time you save.

1. The Amount

The amount you save will be determined by your level of income, and how much you spend for your living expenses and debt. It is our hope that you will increase the amount available for saving as you apply these biblical principles.

2. Rate of Return

The second variable is the rate of interest you earn on an investment. The following table demonstrates how an investment of $1,000 a year grows at various interest rates:

Interest	Year 5	Year 10	Year 20	Year 30	Year 40
6%	5,975	13,972	38,993	83,802	164,048
8%	6,336	15,645	49,423	122,346	279,781
10%	6,716	17,531	63,003	180,943	486,851
12%	7,115	19,655	80,699	270,293	859,142

As you can see, the increase in the rate of return has a remarkable effect on the amount accumulated. A two-percent increase almost doubles the amount over 40 years. However, be careful not to make investments that are too risky in order to achieve a high return. Usually the higher the rate, the higher the risk.

3. Time

Time is the third factor. Answer this question: Who do you think would accumulate more by age sixty-five, a person who started to save $1,000 a year at age 21, saved for eight years, and then completely stopped, or a person who saved $1,000 a year for 37 years who started at age 29? Both earned ten percent. Is it the person who saved a total of $8,000 or the one who saved $37,000? Study the following chart.

	INDIVIDUAL A			INDIVIDUAL B	
Age	Contribution	Year-end Value	Age	Contribution	Year-end Value
21	1,000	1,100	21	0	0
22	1,000	2,310	22	0	0
23	1,000	3,641	23	0	0
24	1,000	5,105	24	0	0
25	1,000	6,716	25	0	0
26	1,000	8,487	26	0	0
27	1,000	10,436	27	0	0
28	1,000	12,579	28	0	0
29	0	13,837	29	1,000	1,100
30	0	15,221	30	1,000	2,310
31	0	16,743	31	1,000	3,641
32	0	18,417	32	1,000	5,105
33	0	20,259	33	1,000	6,716
34	0	22,284	34	1,000	8,487
35	0	24,513	35	1,000	10,436
36	0	26,964	36	1,000	12,579
37	0	29,661	37	1,000	14,937
38	0	32,627	38	1,000	17,531
39	0	35,889	39	1,000	20,384
40	0	39,478	40	1,000	23,523
41	0	43,426	41	1,000	26,975
42	0	47,769	42	1,000	30,772
43	0	52,546	43	1,000	34,950
44	0	57,800	44	1,000	39,545
45	0	63,580	45	1,000	44,599
46	0	69,938	46	1,000	50,159
47	0	76,932	47	1,000	56,275
48	0	84,625	48	1,000	63,003
49	0	93,088	49	1,000	70,403
50	0	103,397	50	1,000	78,543
51	0	112,636	51	1,000	87,497
52	0	123,898	52	1,000	97,347
53	0	136,290	53	1,000	108,182
54	0	149,919	54	1,000	120,100
55	0	164,911	55	1,000	133,210
56	0	181,402	56	1,000	147,631
57	0	199,542	57	1,000	163,494
58	0	219,496	58	1,000	180,943
59	0	241,446	59	1,000	200,138
60	0	265,590	60	1,000	221,252
61	0	292,149	61	1,000	244,477
62	0	321,364	62	1,000	270,024
63	0	353,501	63	1,000	298,127
64	0	388,851	64	1,000	329,039
65	0	**427,736**	65	1,000	**363,043**

Total Investment 8,000   **Total Investment** 37,000

INVESTING NOTES

Incredibly, the person who saved only $8,000 accumulated more because he started saving earlier. The moral of this illustration: Start saving now.

This graph may help you better visualize the benefits of starting now. If a person faithfully saves $2.74 each day—$1,000 a year—and earns 10 percent on the savings, at the end of 40 years the savings will grow to $486,852 and will be earning $4,057 each month in interest alone. Steady plodding pays.

However, if the person waits one year before starting, then saves for thirty-nine years, he will accumulate $45,260 less. Start saving today!

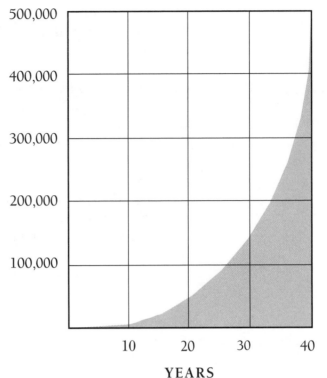

YEARS
$1,000 Invested each year earning 10%

AVOID RISKY INVESTMENTS

"There is another serious problem I have seen everywhere—savings are put into risky investments that turn sour, and soon there is nothing left to pass on to one's son. The man who speculates is soon back to where he began—with nothing" (Ecclesiastes 5:13-15, LB).

Scripture warns of avoiding risky investments, yet each year thousands of people lose money in highly speculative and sometimes fraudulent investments. How many times have you heard of older people losing their life's savings on some get-rich-quick scheme? Sadly, it seems that Christians are particularly vulnerable to such schemes because they trust others who appear to live by the same values they do. We have known of investment scandals in churches, where "wolves in sheep's clothing fleeced the flock." Below three characteristics are listed that will help you identify a potentially risky investment:

1. The prospect of an unusually high profit or interest rate that is "practically guaranteed."
2. The decision to invest must be made quickly. There will be no opportunity to investigate the investment or promoter who is selling the investment. The promoter often will be doing you a "favor" by allowing you to invest.
3. Little will be said about the risks of losing money, and the investment will usually require no effort on your part. Sometimes a portion of the profits will be "dedicated to the Lord's work."

Before participating in any investment, please be patient and prayerfully do your homework.

DIVERSIFY

"Divide your portion to seven or even to eight, for you do not know what misfortune may occur on the earth" (Ecclesiastes 11:2). No investment on this earth is guaranteed. Money can be lost on any investment. The government can make gold illegal. The value of real estate can decrease. Money can be inflated until it is valueless. The stock market can perform well or crash.

My father's friend, Mr. Russell, was very successful in the stock market. When I was a child he used to advise me, "When you grow up, invest in the stock market. It's the one sure way to become financially independent." When I was discharged from the Navy, I came home and met Mr. Russell again. The stock market was in the midst of a significant decline. He said, "I've done a great deal of research on the stock market and the *Titanic*. Do you know the only difference between the two? The *Titanic* had a band!"

The perfect investment does not exist. We need to diversify. Consider the following steps as you diversify. I recommend that you not skip any of the steps. Begin with step one, and then take each step at a time.

STEP 4
Other investments

STEP 3
Home purchase; invest conservatively to meet long-term goals

STEP 2
Three to six months living expenses saved; save for major purchases; develop your business and/or vocational skills

STEP 1
Insurance protection; one month's living expenses saved

COUNTING THE COST

With every investment there are costs: financial costs, time commitments, efforts required, and sometimes even emotional stress. For example, the purchase of a rental house will require time and effort to lease and maintain. If the tenant is irresponsible, you may have to try to collect rent from someone who does not want to pay—talk about emotions! Before you decide on any investment, carefully consider all the costs.

TIMING

"There is an appointed time for everything. And there is a time for every event under heaven" (Ecclesiastes 3:1). The right investment at the wrong time is

the wrong investment. The decision to purchase or sell an investment is best made prayerfully after seeking counsel.

OTHER ISSUES

Gambling and Lotteries

Government-sanctioned lotteries and gambling of all types are sweeping our country. A recent study discovered that people spend 15 times more money on gambling than they donate to churches! The average church member gives $20 a year to foreign missions and the average person gambles $1,174 annually.

Sadly, hundreds of thousands of compulsive gamblers regularly lose their family income. Their stories are heart breaking. The Bible does not specifically prohibit gambling. However, many who gamble do so in an attempt to **get rich quick**. This is a violation of Scripture.

In my opinion, a godly person should never participate in gambling or lotteries—even for entertainment. We should not expose ourselves to the risk of becoming compulsive gamblers, nor should we support an industry that enslaves so many.

Inheritance

Parents should attempt to leave a material inheritance to their children. *"A good man leaves an inheritance to his children's children"* (Proverbs 13:22). The inheritance should not be dispensed until the child has been trained to be a wise steward. *"An inheritance gained hurriedly at the beginning will not be blessed in the end"* (Proverbs 20:21). In my opinion you should make provision in your will for distributing an inheritance over several years or until the heir is mature enough to handle the responsibility of money. Select those you trust to supervise the youth until he is a capable steward. *"Now I say, as long as the heir is a child, he does not differ at all from a slave although he is owner of everything, but he is under guardians and managers until the date set by the father"* (Galatians 4:1-2).

Wills

This week's practical application of "Organizing Your Estate" emphasizes the importance of preparing for your death. As Isaiah told Hezekiah, *"Thus says the Lord, 'Set your house in order, for you shall die'"* (2 Kings 20:1). Someday, should the Lord tarry, you will die. One of the greatest gifts you can leave your family for that emotional time will be an organized estate and a properly prepared will or revocable living trust. If you do not have a current will or trust, please make an appointment this week with an attorney to prepare one.

INSTRUCTIONS FOR THOSE WHO ARE WEALTHY

God loves us with an unfathomable love. Consider what Jesus said in John 15:9, *"Just as the Father has loved me, I have also loved you."* Imagine the depth of love God the Father has for God the Son. In the same way, He loves you! And just as a loving earthly father desires a close relationship with his children,

In my opinion, a godly person should never participate in gambling or lotteries—even for entertainment. We should not expose ourselves to the risk of becoming compulsive gamblers, nor should we support an industry that enslaves so many.

so our heavenly Father hungers for such a relationship with each of us.

God understands human nature perfectly and the particular challenge that wealth presents as a potential barrier to this intimate relationship with Him. If you are wealthy, the Lord is not angry or surprised; rather He intentionally entrusted it to you for a purpose. In 1 Timothy 6:17-19, the Lord issues three instructions to the wealthy that are designed to help them remain undistracted from loving Him.

1. Do Not be Conceited

"Instruct those who are rich in this present world not to be conceited" (1 Timothy 6:17). Wealth naturally tends to produce pride. For several years I drove two vehicles. The first was an old pickup truck that cost $100. It looked as if it cost $100! When I drove that truck to the bank drive-in window to cash a check, I was humble. I knew the cashier was going to carefully check my account to confirm that the driver of that beat up truck had sufficient funds in his account. I was so patient! And when I received the money, I was so grateful. I drove away with a song in my heart and praises on my lips.

My other vehicle was a well-preserved, second-hand automobile that was expensive when it was new. When I drove that car to the bank, I appeared to be a different person. Obviously, I was a man of means who deserved a certain amount of respect. I was not quite as patient when the cashier examined my account, and when I received the money, I was not as grateful. Wealth often leads to conceit.

James 1:9-10 addresses this issue: *"But let the brother of humble circumstances glory in his high position; and let the rich man glory in his humiliation, because like flowering grass he will pass away."* The poor should be encouraged as children of the King of kings, while the rich are to remain humble because life is short. If you are rich, you need the constant reminder to be humble before the Lord and other people.

2. Put No Confidence in Your Assets

"Instruct those who are rich in this present world not . . . to fix their hope on the uncertainty of riches, but on God, who richly supplies us with all things to enjoy" (1 Timothy 6:17). This has been a struggle for me. As we become successful in saving and investing, it is easy for us to trust in those tangible assets we have accumulated. I know that money can buy goods and services. It is our tendency to trust in the seen rather than in the invisible living God. We need to remind ourselves to walk by faith rather than by sight.

3. Give Generously

"Instruct them to do good, to be rich in good works, to be generous and ready to share, storing up for themselves the treasure of a good foundation for the future, so that they may take hold of that which is life indeed" (1 Timothy 6:18-19). The Lord commands the wealthy to be generous and tells them of two benefits of their giving: (1) eternal treasures that they will enjoy in the future, and (2) the blessing of *"taking hold of that which is life indeed."* By exercising generosity they can live the fulfilling life God intends for them.

I was 28 years old when I stumbled upon the only fully guaranteed investment. I started attending a weekly breakfast with several young businessmen and was impressed because they were smart and energetic. But more than that, I was attracted to the quality of their lives. I did not know what asset they owned, but whatever it was, I wanted it.

At that time I was part owner of a successful business, had married my wonderful wife, Bev, and lived in a nice home. I had everything I thought would bring me happiness and a sense of accomplishment, but I had neither. Something was missing in my life.

I was surprised to hear these men speak openly of faith in God. I grew up going to church regularly but it meant nothing to me A friend described how I could enter into a personal, intimate relationship with Jesus Christ. He told me five biblical truths I had never understood before.

1. God Loves You and Wants You to Know Him and Experience a Meaningful Life

God created people in His own image, and He desires an intimate relationship with each of us. My friend shared two passages: *"For God so loved the world, that He gave His only begotten Son, that whoever believes in Him should not perish, but have eternal life"* (John 3:16). *"I [Jesus] came that they might have life, and might have it abundantly"* (John 10:10).

When my son Matthew was in the first grade, he wanted to win the 100-yard dash at his school's field day. That was all he talked about for two months, but there was a problem. His classmate Bobby Dike was faster.

Field day finally arrived. They ran the 50-yard dash first, and Bobby beat Matthew badly. I will never forget when Matthew came up to me with tears in his eyes, pleading, "Daddy, please pray for me in the 100-yard dash. I've just got to win." My heart sank as I nodded.

With the sound of the gun, Matthew got off to a quick start. Halfway through the race he pulled away from the rest of his classmates and won. I lost control of myself! I was jumping and shouting! I had never before experienced such exhilaration. Then it occurred to me: how much I loved my son. Although I love other people, I do not love them enough to give my son to die for them. But that is how much God the Father loved you. He gave His only Son, Jesus Christ, to die for you.

2. Unfortunately, We Are Separated from God

God is holy—which means God is perfect, and He cannot have a relationship with anyone who is not perfect. My friend asked if I had ever sinned—done anything that would disqualify me as perfect. "Many times," I admitted. He explained that every person had sinned, and the consequence of sin was separation from God. *"For all have sinned and fall short of the glory of God"* (Romans 3:23). *"Your sins have cut you off from God"* (Isaiah 59:2, LB).

> God created people in His own image, and He desires an intimate relationship with each of us.

This diagram illustrates our separation from God. An enormous gap separates us from God. Individuals try without success to bridge this gap through their own efforts, such as philosophy, religion, or living a good moral life.

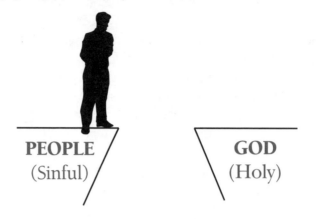

PEOPLE
(Sinful)

GOD
(Holy)

3. God's Only Provision to Bridge this Gap is Jesus Christ

Jesus Christ died on the cross to pay the penalty for our sin. He bridged the gap between us and God. Jesus said, *"I am the way, and the truth, and the life; no one comes to the Father, but through Me"* (John 14:6). *"But God demonstrates His own love towards us, in that while we were yet sinners, Christ died for us"* (Romans 5:8).

This diagram illustrates our union with God through Jesus Christ.

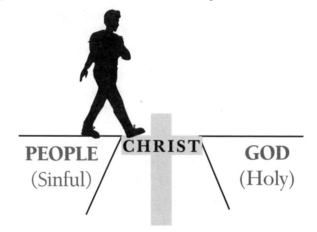

PEOPLE
(Sinful)

CHRIST

GOD
(Holy)

4. This Relationship is a Gift from God

My friend explained that by an act of faith I could receive the free gift of a relationship with God. The transaction appeared totally inequitable. I had learned in business that any time you had two people who were convinced they were getting more than they were giving up, you had a transaction. But now I was being offered a relationship with God, and it was a free gift! *"For by grace you have been saved through faith; and that not of yourselves, it is the gift of God; not as a result of works, that no one should boast"* (Ephesians 2:8-9).

5. We Must Each Receive Jesus Christ Individually

I had only to turn away from (repent of) my sins and ask Jesus Christ to come into my life to be my Savior and Lord. And I did it. As my friends will tell you, I am a very practical person—if something does not work, I discard it quickly. I can tell you from 30 years experience that a relationship with the living God is available to you through Jesus Christ. Nothing I know of compares with the privilege of knowing Christ personally.

If you desire to know the Lord and are not certain whether you have this relationship, I encourage you to receive Christ right now. Pray a prayer similar to this suggested one: "Father God, I need You. I invite Jesus to come into my life as my Savior and Lord and make me the person You want me to be. Thank You for forgiving my sins and giving me the gift of eternal life."

You might fulfill each of the principles in becoming a faithful steward, but without a relationship with Christ, your efforts will be in vain. If you ask Christ into your life, please tell your small group leaders so they will be able to assist you in your spiritual growth.

You might fulfill each of the principles in becoming a faithful steward, but without a relationship with Christ, your efforts will be in vain.

CHILDREN

Parents Are Responsible To Train Their Children To Be Faithful Stewards

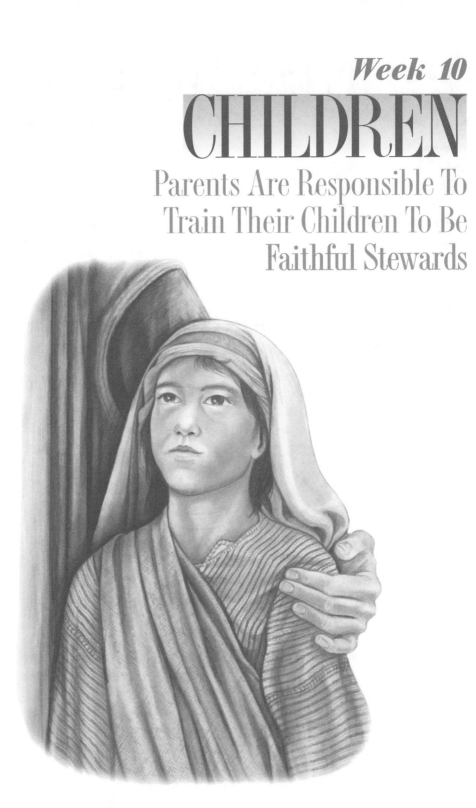

*"Train up a child in the way he should go
and when he is old he will not depart from it."*
Proverbs 22:6

Scripture to Memorize:

"Train up a child in the way he should go, even when he is old he will not depart from it" (Proverbs 22:6).

Practical Application: ☐ Complete the Organizing Your Insurance practical application and continue your budget.

DAY ONE

Read the Investing Notes on pages 120 to 133 and answer:

1. What in the notes proved especially helpful?

2. Carefully study the principle of compounding in the Investing Notes. Assume you earned 10 percent interest and saved $1,000 a year. Approximately how much would you accumulate by age 65 if you started saving today?

    $_____*(refer to the graph on page 127 in the Investing Notes).*

3. Describe the specific steps you intend to take to begin saving:

CHILDREN

Read *Deuteronomy 6:6-7; Deuteronomy 11:18-19; Proverbs 22:6;* **and** *Ephesians 6:4.*

1. According to these passages, who is responsible for teaching children how to handle money from a biblical perspective?

2. Stop and reflect for a few minutes: Describe how well you were prepared to manage money when you first left home as a young person?

NOTE: Answer the questions in **Day Three Homework** through **Day Six Homework** even if you have no children or they no longer live with you.

DAY THREE

1. Describe how you propose to train your children to budget.

2. List four practical suggestions you will teach your children to become wise spenders.

- ■

- ■

- ■

- ■

1. Describe how you are going to teach your children how to save and invest.

   Save—

   Invest—

2. How are you going to train them to conform to the biblical principle of keeping out of debt?

DAY FIVE

1. What methods will you employ to train your children to be generous, cheerful givers?

1. List four suggestions to teach your children to work hard and to work "as unto the Lord."

■

■

■

■

 Please write your prayer requests in your prayer log before coming to class.

I will take the following action as a result of this week's study:

CHILDREN

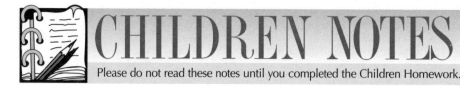

CHILDREN NOTES

Please do not read these notes until you completed the Children Homework.

In 1904 the country of Wales experienced a remarkable revival. Thousands of people were introduced to Christ in a period of nine months, and the results were dramatic! Bars closed because of lack of business. Policemen exchanged their weapons for white gloves as a witness that crime disappeared. Horses did not understand their drivers as profanity was no longer uttered. Wales was so evangelically minded that it sent missionaries all over the world.

One of those missionaries traveled to Argentina where on the streets he led a young boy to Christ. The boy's name was Luis Palau. He has since become known as the "Billy Graham" of Latin America. Palau decided in the early 1970s to go to Wales and express his thankfulness to that people for helping lead him to Christ. What he discovered was astonishing. Less than one-half of one percent of the Welsh attended church. Divorce was at an all-time high, and crime was increasing. Many churches had been converted to bars, and rugby had replaced Christianity as the national passion.

As a result of this experience, Palau produced a film entitled *God Has No Grandchildren*. The thrust of the film is that each generation is responsible for passing on the faith to the next. In Wales, despite tremendous spiritual vitality, the impact of Christianity had all but disappeared in 70 years.

Parents had failed to pass their faith on to their children. Each generation is responsible for passing on the gospel and the truths of Scripture, including God's financial principles, to its children. Proverbs 22:6 reads, *"Train up a child in the way he should go, even when he is old he will not depart from it."*

Answer this question: When you left home, how well prepared were you to make financial decisions? Parents and teachers spend 18 to 22 years preparing our youth for occupations, but generally less than a few hours teaching children the value and use of the money they will earn during their careers. To teach biblical principles of handling money, parents should use these three methods: verbal communication, modeling, and practical experience.

> *Each generation is responsible for passing on the gospel and truths of Scripture, including God's financial priniples, to its children.*

VERBAL COMMUNICATION

The Lord charged the Israelites, *"And these words, which I am commanding you today, shall be on your heart; and you shall teach them diligently to your sons and shall talk of them when you sit in your house and when you walk by the way and when you lie down and when you rise up"* (Deuteronomy 6:6-7). We must verbally instruct our children in the ways of the Lord, but children need more than mere verbal instruction; they also need a good example.

MODELING

Children soak up parental attitudes toward money like a sponge soaks up water. Parents need to be models of how to handle money faithfully. Paul recognized the importance of example when he said, *"Be imitators of me, just as I also am of Christ"* (1 Corinthians 11:1). The Lord used both of these techniques. He gave us His written word, the Bible, and also sent the perfect model, Jesus Christ, to demonstrate how we should live.

Luke 6:40 is a challenging passage for parents. It reads, *"Everyone, after he has been fully trained, will be like his teacher."* Another way of saying this is that we can teach what we believe, but we only reproduce who we are. We must be good models.

PRACTICAL EXPERIENCES

Children then need to be given opportunities to apply what they have heard and seen. There are learning experiences which benefit the child in the area of money management (the art of wise spending) and money making (the value of work).

LEARNING EXPERIENCES IN MONEY MANAGEMENT

Learning to handle money should be part of a child's education. This is a part which the parents must direct themselves and not delegate to teachers, because spending experiences are found outside the classroom. Consider five areas where this is possible:

1. Income

As soon as the child is ready for school, he should begin to receive an income to manage. Parents need to decide whether the child must earn the income, or if they wish to give an allowance.

The amount of the income will vary according to as the child's age, his ability to earn, and the financial circumstances of the family. However, the amount of the income is not as important as the responsibility of handling money. At first it is a new experience, and the child will make many mistakes. Do not hesitate to let the "law of natural consequences" run its course. You are going to be tempted to help the child when he spends all the income the first day on an unwise purchase. You will not like the fact that he has to live the rest of the week without the other things he wants and maybe needs. *But do not bail him out!* His mistakes will be his best teacher.

Parents should establish boundaries and offer advice on how to spend money, but your child must have freedom of choice within those boundaries. Excessive restrictions will only reduce opportunities to learn. The first few pennies and nickels will make a lasting impression. Every Saturday morning I used to bicycle to the corner store with my son, Matthew, to buy him a pack of his favorite gum. Despite my advice, the entire pack would be consumed that first day.

When he started to earn money, we decided that Matthew would have to buy his own gum. I will never forget the pained expression on his face as he came out of the store with his first purchase that cost him two weeks' income. "Daddy, this gum cost me all my money!" he yelled. That pack of gum was rationed with tender care and lasted more than a week. Parents should slowly increase the allowance as the child grows in his ability and demonstrates wise spending patterns.

2. Budgeting

When children start to receive an income, teach them how to budget. Begin with a simple system consisting of a three-compartment bank, each compartment labeled separately: give, save and spend. The child distributes a portion of his income into each compartment. Thus a simple budget is established by using visual control. Even a six-year-old can understand this method, because when there is no more money to spend, the bank is empty!

As the child matures, he should participate in every aspect of the family budget. It will help him understand the limitations of the family income and how to stretch the money to meet family needs.

At first a child may think the family has so much money it is impossible to spend it all. To help children visualize the budget, have the family income converted to a sack of one dollar bills. Place these on the table during family budget time and divide the "income" pile into the various "expense" piles representing the categories of spending. It is often difficult for children to grasp numbers because they are abstract. The dollars will be a tangible way for them to understand the family budget.

When a child becomes a teenager, he or she should begin a written budget It is wise to train teens to use one of the budgeting software programs that are available. During the budget training, teach your child to become a wise consumer. Teach shopping skills, the ability to distinguish needs from wants, and the importance of waiting on the Lord to provide. Warn the child about the powerful influence of advertising and the danger of impulse spending.

3. Saving and Investing

The habit of saving should be established as soon as the child receives an income. It is helpful to open a savings account in the child's name at this time. As children mature, expose them to various types of investments: stocks, bonds, real estate, etc. Also, teach your children the benefits of compounding interest. If they grasp this concept and become faithful savers, they will enjoy financial stability as adults. Parents should demonstrate this principle by saving for something that will directly affect and benefit the children, such as a family vacation. Use a graph the children can fill in so they can visually chart the progress of saving.

Children should have both short-term and long-term saving programs. The younger the child, the more important are short-term achievable goals. To a four-year-old, a week seems like a lifetime to save for a small purchase. They will not understand saving for their future education, but will get excited about saving for a small toy. Long-term saving, such as for education and the first car, should be a requirement. Some parents find it motivating to their child if they match their child's contribution to their long-term savings.

4. Debt

It is also important to teach the cost of money and how difficult it is to get out of debt. A father loaned his son and daughter the money to buy bicycles. He drew up a credit agreement with a schedule for repayment of the loan, including the interest charged. After they went through the long, difficult process of paying off the loan, the family celebrated with a "mortgage burning" ceremony. The father said that his children appreciated those bikes more than any of their other possessions and vowed to avoid debt in the future.

5. Giving

The best time to establish the personal habit of giving is when a child is young. It is helpful for children to give a portion of their gifts to a need they can see. For example, a child understands the impact of his gift when his contribution is helping to build the church he can see under construction or buying food for a needy family he knows.

Richard Halverson, U. S. Senate chaplain, gave his son, Chris, this rich heritage as a child. Chris and his brother gave money to support Kim, a Korean orphan who had lost his sight during the Korean War. Chris was taught to feel that Kim was like an adopted brother. One Christmas, Chris bought Kim a harmonica. It was Kim's first personal possession. He cherished this gift from Chris and learned to play it well. Today, Kim is an evangelist and his presentation of the gospel includes playing the harmonica. By being trained to give as a youth, Chris experienced firsthand the value of meeting people's needs, and as a result of faithful giving, seeing God change lives.

When your child is a teenager, a family or church mission trip to a Third World country can be a powerful experience. Direct exposure to abject poverty can initiate a lifetime of giving to the poor. We also recommend a family time each week for dedicating that week's gifts to the Lord. It is important for children to participate in this time of dedication and worship. The more involvement children can have in the proper handling of money, the better habits they will have as adults.

LEARNING EXPERIENCES IN MONEY MAKING

Parents also have the responsibility to train children in the value of work and in the development of proper work habits. If the child responds and learns how to work with the proper attitude, he or she will become a valuable commodity in the job market. Good employees are difficult to find. Clearly, children need to learn the dignity and habit of work. There are four areas to consider in this training:

1. Learning Routine Responsibilities

The best way for a child to become faithful in work is to establish the habit of daily household chores. These are chores that each member of the family is expected to perform. For example, my daughter carried out the garbage and washed the dishes, and my son cleaned the floors.

2. Expose Your Children to Your Work

Many children do not know how their father or mother earns the family income. A friend asked his father what he did at work. "I make money," the father responded. "For a long time I thought my dad actually made dollar bills. My mother would ask Dad, 'How much did you draw this week?' I thought he was a great artist to be able to do all that detailed artwork."

An important way to teach the value of work is to expose the child to the parents' means of making a living. If your children cannot visit you at work, at least take the time to explain your job to them. For parents who manage their own businesses, children should be encouraged to participate.

One word of advice: Because most children are not with their parents at work, parents' work attitudes and habits around the home will be a major modeling influence. If a parent works hard away from home but complains about washing the dishes at home, what is being communicated to the children about work? Examine your work attitudes and activities at home to insure that you are properly influencing your children to be godly workers.

3. Earning Extra Money

You should encourage your child to do extra work to earn money. A good rule of thumb is to pay the child a fair wage for the work you would have to hire someone to do. For example, if your car needs washing and your son needs some extra money and wants to wash it, let him. Be happy to pay him rather than the man at the car wash.

4. Working for Others

A paper route, baby-sitting, janitorial work, or waiting on tables will be an education. A job gives a child an opportunity to enter into an employee-employer relationship and to earn extra money. The objective of teaching your child the value of work is to build and discipline his character. A working child with the proper attitude will be a more satisfied individual. He will grow up with more respect for the value of money and the effort required to earn it.

5. Career Direct—YES!

The Career Direct—Youth Exploration Survey™ helps point students ages 13-16 toward an exciting future career. It covers four areas: personality, vocational interests, abilities, and priorities. It is designed to be fun, informative, interactive, and biblically based and can be used for individual or small-group study. To order, contact CROWN.

DEDICATION, DEPENDENCY, DANGER AND DESTRUCTION

Dedication of Dad

Fathers in our country spend less time with their children than parents in almost every other nation of the world. According to a survey, fathers spend an average of only 37 seconds a day communicating with their sons! David and Eli were both godly men who had remarkably productive careers. Yet both lost sons through careless fathering.

If children are going to thrive, it will be because parents place their children high on their list of priorities, consistently reserving an adequate portion of their time and energy for leadership within their homes. Fathers, I plead with you to seize the opportunity to train your children. You can literally influence generations.

Single mothers are increasingly common. If you are one, I appreciate the added demands you face. But please be encouraged. Some of the most responsible children I have ever met have been raised by godly mothers, and I pray that the Lord will bless your efforts.

Dependency on Prayer

One of the more valuable lessons you can teach your children is to seek the Lord's guidance and to experience His provision through prayer. The Lord wants to demonstrate that He is alive and actively involved in each of our lives. One way He does this is by answering our prayers. Because of our affluent society, we often rob ourselves of this opportunity. We can buy things or charge purchases without prayerfully allowing the Lord to supply them. A couple who wanted to impress their son with the importance of praying for God's provision decided to ask him to pray for some shirts he needed. After several months, a friend in the clothing business called to ask if their son needed shirts because he had excess inventory in his size. They excitedly responded, "Absolutely!" Their friend brought 25 shirts to their home! That evening as their son began to pray for his shirts, the father said, "You don't have to pray for those shirts any longer. God has answered your prayers." They brought the shirts out one-by-one. By the twenty-fifth shirt, their son thought God was in the shirt business. We need to be seeking ways we can experience the reality of God in the area of our spending, and communicate this value to our children.

Danger of Television and the Internet

Television and the "dark side" of the Internet have affected children and their values in ways we have not yet begun to understand. Consider these statistics: by the time the typical teenager graduates from high school, he has spent 10,800 hours in class and 15,000 hours in front of the "tube." Children spend more time watching television or surfing the net (30 to 50 hours per week) than any other activity except sleeping, and they will see about a million commercials by age 20. A survey asked children if they would rather give up television or their fathers—44 percent responded they would rather have television than their fathers.

Most damage comes, not from television programs or commercials that directly attack biblical standards, but from those who make anti-scriptural assumptions and whose attack is indirect. The Internet can bring pornography, gambling, and other destructive information into the home. The influence of television and the Internet on children is so potentially dangerous that parents cannot afford to ignore it. Rather they must regulate its use if they are to be successful in training their children to be faithful stewards.

Destruction Caused by Overindulgence

When it comes to money, parents are always on a tightrope trying to keep a proper balance. As parents we can be too miserly with money, but in our affluent culture, more often we are overindulgent. How many of us know of a father who once sold newspapers to earn a bicycle and now has a 17-year-old son driving a sports car? Overindulgence with money is destructive. It retards the development of a child's character and destroys the need for initiative and motivation. Too often it creates in children a constant expectation to be given things without giving anything in return.

Grandparents

If you are a grandparent, you have a unique opportunity to influence your grandchildren. An inheritance is more than just material possessions. A godly inheritance includes a legacy of teaching the younger generation to understand God's way. We strongly recommend that parents meet with grandparents and together design a strategy for this training. It is important for grandparents to play a role in which they confirm and complement the objectives of the parents. Too often parents and grandparents have not reached agreement on how to train the next generation. This can lead to bruised relationships and ineffective training.

> *Overindulgence with money is destructive. It retards the development of a child's character and destroys the need for initiative and motivation.*

STRATEGY FOR INDEPENDENCE

Finally, we need to establish a strategy for independence. Lyle and Marge Nelsen have four of the most mature and responsible children I have ever met. Their strategy has been to work toward having each child independently managing all of his own finances (with the exception of food and shelter) by his senior year in high school. In this way they could be available to advise the children as they learned to make spending decisions. Let us review the three steps for training children:

1. **Verbally communicate** biblical principles of handling money. It would be wise to have your children go through one of the CROWN youth studies, with you serving as their teacher.
2. Parents, become **models of financial faithfulness**, allowing your children to observe closely how you apply these principles.
3. **Create practical opportunities** for your children to experience God's financial principles. These experiences should be tangible enough to be understood. Each child has an individual personality and temperament. One child may spend wildly, yet be very generous; another may save everything and never want to give. You need to study your children's personalities carefully and tailor the training to fit the child.

As the people of Wales discovered, God has no grandchildren. Passing our faith in Christ to the next generation can be compared to a relay race. Any track coach will tell you relay races can be won or lost in the passing of the baton from one runner to another. Seldom is the baton dropped once it is firmly in the grasp of a sprinting runner. If it is going to be dropped, it is in the exchange between the runners. As parents we have the responsibility to pass the baton of practical biblical truths to our children. At times during the training it seems as if there is little progress. But be *consistent and persistent!*

I have yet to meet an adult whose parents lived these biblical financial principles and taught them systematically to their children. As an unfortunate consequence of this lack of training, children left home ill-equipped to manage their financial future according to God's principles. I pray our generation will leave our children the blessed legacy of financial faithfulness.

STUDIES FOR CHILDREN

To help parents and teachers train children to handle money God's way, CROWN FINANCIAL MINISTRIES has developed four outstanding studies. The three studies for younger children may be taught in a variety of settings—one-on-one, in small groups and, in a classroom. No special teacher training is required for these studies.

The **ABC'S of Handling Money God's Way** (for children ages 7 and younger) and **The Secret** (for children 8 to 12) are fully illustrated storybooks that make learning basic financial principles fun and exciting! The Leader's Guide for each book provides a wide variety of activities that reinforce these principles.

Teens love **God's Way of Handling Money.** The practical applications at the end of each chapter are designed to help teens begin habits that will set them on a lifelong journey of handling money God's way.

CROWN'S **Collegiate Edition** is an excellent study to teach God's perspective of money at this formative time of their lives. It may be taught in a small group or college classroom.

See the order form in the *Practical Application Workbook* or contact:

CROWN FINANCIAL MINISTRIES
PO Box 100
Gainesville GA 30503-0100
1-800-722-1976
www.crown.org

PAUL—
CONTENT IN EVERY CIRCUMSTANCE

"For I have learned to be content in whatever circumstances I am.
I know how to get along with humble means, and I also know
how to live in prosperity."
Philippians 4:11-12

PERSPECTIVE HOMEWORK

Scripture to Memorize:

"For I have learned to be content in whatever circumstances I am. I know how to get along with humble means, and I also know how to live in prosperity; in any and every circumstance I have learned the secret of being filled and going hungry, both of having abundance and suffering need. I can do all things through Him who strengthens me" (Philippians 4:11-13).

Practical Application: ☐ Complete the Organizing Your Children practical application.

> Note: Think about your prayer request for the last class. It should be a "long-term" request the others can pray when they think of you.

DAY ONE

Read the Children Notes on pages 140 to 147 and answer:

What ideas from the notes will you incorporate in training children to be faithful stewards?

DAY TWO

Read *Genesis 13:5-11; Matthew 13:7; 22,* and *Matthew 19:16-23.*

Each passage contains a danger associated with riches. Identify the danger from each verse and share one insight that could significantly alter or impact your thinking.

Genesis 13:5-11—

Matthew 13:7, 22—

Matthew 19:16-23—

Significant insight:

Read *Deuteronomy 30:15-16; Joshua 1:8;* **and** *Hebrews 11:36-40.*

1. What do each of these passages communicate to you about financial prosperity for the believer?

   Deuteronomy 30:15-16—

   Joshua 1:8—

   Hebrews 11:36-40—

Reflect on the lives of Job, Joseph, David, and Paul.

2. Did these men ever experience periods of financial abundance and at other times a lack of financial prosperity?

3. Was their lack of financial prosperity a result of sin or lack of faith?

4. Should all Christians always prosper financially? Why?

PERSPECTIVE

Then read *Psalm 73:1-20.*

5. What does this passage tell you about the prosperity of the wicked?

6. How does this impact your thinking?

DAY FOUR

Read *Luke 3:14; Philippians 4:11-13;* **and** *1 Timothy 6:6-8.*

1. What do each of these passages communicate to you about contentment?

    Luke 3:14—

    Philippians 4:11-13—

    1 Timothy 6:6-8—

2. How does our culture discourage contentment?

3. How do you propose to practice contentment?

Read *Matthew 5:25-26* **and** *Romans 13:1-7* **and answer:**

1. Does the Lord require us to pay taxes to the government? Why?

2. Do you think it is biblically permissible to reduce your taxes by using legal tax deductions? Why?

Read *James 2:1-9.*

3. What does Scripture say about partiality (showing favoritism)?

4. Are you guilty of partiality based on a person's financial, educational, or social status?

Read *Romans 12:16* **and** *Philippians 2:3.*

5. How do you plan to overcome partiality?

PERSPECTIVE

Read Mark 8:36-37; Acts 4:32-37; and 1 Thessalonians 4:11-12.

1. What do these passages communicate to you about lifestyle?

    Mark 8:36-37—

    Acts 4:32-37—

    1 Thessalonians 4:11-12—

2. How do the following factors influence your present spending and lifestyle?

    ▪ Comparing your lifestyle with that of friends and other people —

    ▪ Television, magazines, catalogues, and other advertisements—

    ▪ Your study of the Bible—

    ▪ Your commitment to Christ and to things that are important to Him—

3. Do you sense that the Lord would have you alter any part of your standard of living? If so, what?

 Please write your prayer requests in your prayer log before coming to class.

 I will take the following action as a result of this week's study:

PERSPECTIVE NOTES 👑

Please do not read these notes until you completed the Perspective Homework.

In this chapter we will explore the Lord's perspective on a wide variety of issues: the dangers of wealth, determining lifestyle, understanding prosperity, avoiding litigation, paying taxes, and overcoming partiality.

DANGERS OF WEALTH

Remember, that God loves you deeply and He wants to enjoy an intimate, vibrant relationship with you. Because of His love for us, the Lord reveals in Scripture a number of dangers associated with wealth that can pose a threat to our relationship with Him and other people. First, wealth tends to separate people. Abram and Lot were relatives who became wealthy. This ultimately caused them to move away from each other. *"Now Abram was very rich in livestock, in silver and in gold . . . [Lot] also had flocks and herds and tents. And the land could not sustain them while dwelling together; for their possessions were so great that they were not able to remain together"* (Genesis 13:2, 5-7). Most of us know friends or family members who have allowed conflicts over money to damage or destroy their relationships.

Secondly, it is easy for those who are rich to become proud and turn from God. *"For when I [the Lord] bring them into the land flowing with milk and honey, which I swore to their fathers, and they have eaten and are satisfied and become prosperous, then they will turn to other gods and serve them, and spurn Me"* (Deuteronomy 31:20). Someone once observed, "For every 99 who can be poor and remain close to Christ, only one person can become wealthy and maintain close fellowship with Him." It must be human nature to cling to the Lord when it's obvious that He must provide our needs. Once people become wealthy, they often take the Lord for granted because they no longer think they have as much need of Him. Paul warned Timothy, *"Instruct those who are rich in this present world not to be conceited or to fix their hope on the uncertainty of riches, but on God"* (1 Timothy 6:17).

Thirdly, it is difficult for the rich to come to know Jesus Christ as their Savior. *"And Jesus said to His disciples, 'Truly I say to you, it is hard for a rich man to enter the kingdom of heaven'"* (Matthew 19:23). Again, I think this is because the rich generally have less of a felt need for God. Riches also can destroy a spiritually fruitful life. *"And the one on whom seed was sown among the thorns, this is the man who hears the word, and the worry of the world, and the deceitfulness of riches choke the word, and it becomes unfruitful"* (Matthew 13:22). Riches are deceitful because they are tangible and can

Riches are deceitful because they are tangible and can blind us from the reality of the unseen Lord. They seem to be able to do things that only Christ can really do.

blind us from the reality of the unseen Lord. They seem to be able to do things that only Christ can really do.

The Bible does not demand one standard of living for everyone. In Scripture, godly people are represented in all walks of life, and the Lord still places His people strategically in every level of society—rich and poor. We encourage you to evaluate your standard of living. To help your thinking, let's examine several scriptural principles that should influence your lifestyle.

1. Learn to Be Content

The apostle Paul wrote in 1 Timothy 6:8: *"And if we have food and covering* [clothes and shelter], *with these we shall be content."* If this were an adver-

tisement, it would read something like this, "If you can afford the finest food, wear the latest fashions, drive the newest luxury automobile, live in a beautiful home, then you will be happy." Our consumption-oriented society operates on the assumptions that more is always better and happiness is based on acquiring.

The word "contentment" is mentioned seven times in Scripture, and six times it has to do with money. Paul wrote, *"I have learned to be content in whatever circumstances I am. I know how to get along with humble means, and I also know how to live in prosperity; in any and every circumstance I have learned the secret of being filled and going hungry, both of having abundance and suffering need. I can do all things through Him who strengthens me"* (Philippians 4:11-13). Paul "learned" to be content. We are not born content; rather, we learn contentment.

There are three elements to the secret of contentment as illustrated in the diagram below:

| **KNOWING** what God requires of us in handling money and possessions | + | **DOING** those requirements | + | **TRUSTING** God to provide exactly what He knows is best | = | **CONTENTMENT** |

Note carefully that it is not just knowing these things that brings contentment; it is doing them. Once we have been faithful in the doing, we can be content in knowing that our loving, heavenly Father will entrust the precise quantity of possessions He knows will be best for us at any particular time—whether much or little. Biblical contentment is not to be equated with laziness, or apathy. Because we serve the living and dynamic God, Christians should always be improving. Contentment does not exclude properly motivated ambition. In fact, I believe we should have a burning desire to be increasingly faithful stewards of the talents and possessions entrusted to us.

Biblical contentment is an inner peace that accepts what God has chosen for our present vocation, station in life, and financial situation. Hebrews 13:5 emphasizes this: *"Let your way of life be free from the love of money, being content with what you have; for He Himself has said, 'I will never desert you, nor will I ever forsake you.'"*

2. Learn to Avoid Coveting

Coveting means to crave another person's property, and it is expressly prohibited throughout Scripture. The last of the Ten Commandments reads, *"You shall not covet your neighbor's house; you shall not covet your neighbor's wife or his male servant or his female servant or his ox or his donkey or anything that belongs to your neighbor"* (Exodus 20:17). Note the broad application: *"or anything that belongs to your neighbor."* In other words, we are commanded not to covet anything that belongs to anyone!

Greed is similar to coveting. *"But do not let immorality or any impurity or greed even be named among you. . . . For this you know with certainty, that no immoral or impure person or covetous man, who is an idolater, has an inheritance in the kingdom of Christ and God"* (Ephesians 5:3, 5).

A greedy or covetous person is an idolater. Coveting and greed have been called the silent sins. Rarely are they confronted, but I believe they are among the most widespread sins of today. When I began studying what the Bible taught about money, I was overwhelmed by the extent of my own coveting. Ask the Lord to show you if you are guilty of coveting that which is another's. If so, ask the Lord to change your heart.

3. If Only . . .

Have you ever felt that "if only" you were in a more prestigious position or had more money, then you could accomplish really significant things for the Lord? Let's examine two men who lived in Rome and were at different ends of the economic spectrum. In the coliseum, everyone would stand waiting for Caesar before the gladiator contests were permitted to begin. When Caesar arrived, he was greeted with thunderous shouts of "Hail Caesar!" He had more power, prestige and wealth than anyone else living at that time. He was worshipped as though he were a god.

In a different part of Rome another man was in much different circumstances. He was in prison and chained to guards. He invested his time praying and writing to his friends. His name was Paul. One man lived in a beautiful palace, the other lived in a dingy cell. One had almost unlimited wealth, the other had almost nothing. One was the center of attention, the other was virtually ignored.

Almost 2,000 years later, people around the world recognize which of these two men made the eternally important contribution, and they honor him by naming their children—after the prisoner. Being used by Christ in a significant way has nothing to do with a high position or great riches. It has everything to do with a willingness to allow Christ to be your Lord.

The word "contentment" is mentioned seven times in Scripture, and six times it has to do with money.

4. Do Not Determine Your Lifestyle By Comparing it to Others

Some use comparison to justify spending more than they should. Many have suffered financially because they tried but could not afford to "keep up with the Joneses." Someone once said, "You can never keep up with the Joneses. Just about the time you've caught them, they go deeper in debt to buy more things!" If you are wealthy, your lifestyle should be based on the conviction that the Lord wants you to have a certain standard of living, and not one necessarily dictated by the maximum you can afford.

5. Freely Enjoy Whatever You Spend in the "Spirit"

Prayerfully submit spending decisions to the Lord. Everything we possess is owned by the Lord, and we should spend to please Him and not for a selfish purpose. Seeking the Lord's direction in spending does not mean that we will never spend for anything other than a basic necessity.

During the Christmas season several years ago, my wife asked me to purchase a kitchen appliance that I considered extravagant. However, I promised to seek the Lord's direction. As we prayed, He made it clear that we should purchase the appliance, which we have thoroughly enjoyed. *"For everything created by God is good, and nothing is to be rejected, if it is received with gratitude"* (1 Timothy 4:4).

6. How Much is Enough?

What should you do after you have achieved your God-given financial goals, and the income from your savings and investments is sufficient to meet your living expenses? Consider these possibilities: (1) If you continue working for an income, give all your salary to the work of Christ. This will free you from the temptation to hoard. (2) If the Lord wants you to work for a particular ministry, you can volunteer your time without requiring compensation.

7. Make an Effort to Live More Simply

Every possession requires time and often money to maintain. Too many or the wrong types of possessions can demand so much time or money that they harm our relationships with the Lord and our families. A quiet, simple life is the safest environment for us to be able to invest enough time to nurture our relationship with the Lord. First Thessalonians 4:11-12 counsels, *"Make it your ambition to lead a quiet life and attend to your own business and work with your hands, just as we commanded you; so that you may behave properly toward outsiders and not be in any need."*

Do not become unduly encumbered with the cares of this life. *"Suffer hardship with me, as a good soldier of Christ Jesus. No soldier in active service entangles himself in the affairs of everyday life, so that he may please the one who enlisted him as a soldier"* (2 Timothy 2:3-4).

8. Needs Should be Met Within the Body of Christ

The early church was a model of having needs met. *"This [gift] is not for the ease of others and for your affliction, but by way of equality— at this present time your abundance being a supply for their want, that their abundance also may*

PERSPECTIVE NOTES

become a supply for your want, that there may be equality; as it is written, 'He who gathered much did not have too much, and he who gathered little had no lack'" (2 Corinthians 8:13-15). This lifestyle is the perfect environment for spiritual revival. Acts 4:32-35: *"And the congregation of those who believed were of one heart and soul; and not one of them claimed that anything belonging to him was his own; but all things were common property to them. . . . For there was not a needy person among them, for all who were owners of lands or houses would sell them and bring the proceeds of the sales, and lay them at the apostles' feet; and they would be distributed to each, as any had need."*

9. Success is Meaningless Apart from Serving Jesus Christ

Leslie Flynn in his book, *Your God and Your Gold,* pointed out: "Solomon, the author of Ecclesiastes, had an annual income of more than $35 million. He lived in a palace that took thirteen years to build. He owned 40,000 stalls of horses. He sat on an ivory throne overlaid with gold. He drank from gold cups. The daily menu of his household included a 100 sheep and 30 oxen in addition to deer and fowl."

Obviously, Solomon was in a position to evaluate whether money and possessions would bring true fulfillment. He concluded, *"Vanity of vanities...all is vanity!"* (Ecclesiastes 12:8). Nothing, even extraordinary success, can replace the value of our relationship with the Lord. Ask yourself this question: Are you sacrificing an intimate relationship with Christ in the pursuit of wealth? *"For what does it profit a man to gain the whole world, and forfeit his soul"* (Mark 8:36)?

10. Do Not be Conformed to this World

Romans 12:2 begins with this command, *"Do not be conformed to this world."* The Amplified Bible reads this way: *"Do not be conformed to this world—this age, fashioned after and adapted to its external, superficial customs"* (Romans 12:2). We live in what probably is the most affluent culture in the history of the world. We are constantly bombarded with costly, manipulative advertising. The purpose of advertising is to prompt us to spend money. Advertisers usually stress the importance of image rather than function. For example, automobile ads rarely focus on a car as reliable transportation. Instead, an image of status or sex appeal is projected.

Reflect on the claims of TV commercials. No matter what the product—clothing, deodorants, credit cards, you name it—the message is communicated that the "fulfilling, beautiful, wrinkle-free life" can be ours if we are willing to buy it. Unfortunately, to some extent this media onslaught has influenced all of us. Author George Fooshee so aptly states, "People buy things they do not need with money they do not have to impress people they do not even like."

This graph depicts how the artificial, media-generated lifestyle influences our lives. The bottom

Courtesy Patrick Morley

'My problem has been that everytime prosperity was just around the corner, so was the shopping center.'

curve represents our income—what we can really afford to buy. The next curve illustrates what we actually spend. We make up the difference between our income and spending by the use of debt, which creates financial pressure and anxiety. The top of the graph demonstrates what advertisers tell us to buy. It is an image-conscious lifestyle that claims to satisfy the human heart's deepest needs. When we want to live this counterfeit dream but cannot afford it, we suffer discontentment.

None of us is immune to this message. A sharp-looking van in a commercial caught my eye. Our family had a second-hand, eleven-year-old station wagon painted an unattractive yellow. This advertised vehicle was perfect—even the right color! I found myself studying beautiful brochures, admiring new vans on the highway, and daydreaming about driving one. I was hooked! The yellow station wagon seemed to get more unsightly every day, while the van went from an "I-want-it" to an "I-need-it" item.

I was about to buy the van, when I decided to seek the counsel of Jack Norman, a car dealer and friend. He asked how many miles the station wagon had been driven. "Fifty-five thousand miles," I responded. He said, "The station wagon is in good condition and should easily last you another eight years!" I didn't want to hear that, but finally agreed with him. He saved me thousands of dollars in a few minutes. Moreover, the moment the decision was made to keep the yellow station wagon, I lost the desire for the van, and it no longer dominated my thinking. Interestingly enough, the yellow station wagon got better-looking!

From time to time we all get hooked on something we think we must buy. Once hooked, it is easy to rationalize a purchase of anything. Remember to seek the Lord's guidance and godly counsel when making a spending decision.

POVERTY, PROSPERITY OR STEWARDSHIP?

Many Christians embrace one of two extremes about finances. On one end of the spectrum, some believe that godliness can only occur in poverty. However, money can be used for good or evil. A number of godly people in Scripture were among the wealthiest individuals of their day. In the Old Testament the Lord extended the reward of abundance for obedience, while the threat of poverty was one of the consequences of disobedience. Deuteronomy 30:15-16 reads, *"I have set before you today life and prosperity, and death and adversity; in that I command you today to love the Lord your God, to walk in His ways and to keep His commandments . . . that the Lord your God may bless you."*

Moreover, Psalm 35:27 reads, *"The Lord . . . delights in the prosperity of His servant."* We may pray for prosperity when our relationship with the Lord is healthy, and we have a proper perspective of possessions. *"Beloved, I pray that in all respects you may prosper and be in good health, just as your soul prospers"* (3 John 2). The Bible does not say that a godly person must live in poverty. A godly person may have material resources.

At the other end of spectrum lies the belief that all Christians who truly have faith will always prosper. This extreme is also in error. Study the life of Joseph. He is the classic example of a faithful person who experienced prosperity and poverty. He was born into a prosperous family, then was thrown into a pit, and finally sold into slavery by his jealous brothers. While Joseph was a slave, his master promoted him to be head of his household. Later he made the righteous decision not to commit adultery with his master's wife, yet was thrown in jail for years because of that decision. In God's timing he was ultimately elevated to Prime Minister of Egypt.

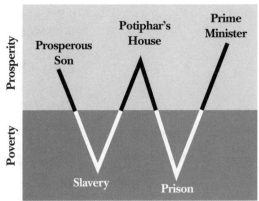

The guideline for prosperity is found in Joshua 1:8, *"This book of the law shall not depart from your mouth, but you shall meditate on it day and night so that you may be careful to do according to all that is written in it; for then you will make your way prosperous, and then you will have success."*

Two requirements for prosperity become apparent from studying this passage. You must meditate on the Scriptures, engraving them on your mind and heart; and you are required to do all that is written in them. Once you have fulfilled these obligations, you place yourself in the position to be blessed financially, but there is no guarantee that the godly will always experience financial prosperity. There are four reasons the godly may not prosper:

1. Violating Scriptural Principles
Look again at Joshua 1:8. There is the requirement to do **all** that is written in the Bible. You may be giving generously but acting dishonestly. You may be honest but not fulfilling your work responsibilities. You may be a faithful employee but head-over-heels in debt. You may be completely out of debt but not giving. One of the biggest benefits of this study is that we explore what the entire Bible teaches about money. Those who do not understand all the requirements often neglect critical areas of responsibility unknowingly and suffer financially.

2. Building Godly Character
Romans 5:3-4 reads, *"Tribulation brings about perseverance, and perseverance, proven character."* Many godly people in the Bible lived righteously, yet lost their possessions. David became a national hero after slaying Goliath. David served faithfully, only to be forced to flee for his life from a tormented King Saul. Job lost his children and possessions in the space of a few moments and was described as a *"blameless and upright man, fearing God and turning away from evil"* (Job 1:8). Paul learned the secret of contentment while being held captive in chains and suffering want, even though he was righteous.

God sometimes molds our character by allowing us to experience difficult circumstances. An example of how the Lord develops character in a people before prospering them is found in Deuteronomy 8:16-18: *"In the wilderness He fed you manna which your fathers did not know, that He might humble you and that He might test you, to do good for you in the end. Otherwise, you may say in your heart, 'My power and the strength of my hand made me this wealth.' But you shall remember the Lord your God, for it is He who is giving you power to make wealth.*" The children of Israel needed to be humbled before they could handle wealth. Our Father knows us better than we know ourselves. In His infinite wisdom He knows exactly how much He can entrust to us at any time without it harming our relationship with Him.

3. Our Dependence and His Discipline

A father was carrying his two-year-old child as he waded in a lake. When they were close to shore, the child was unconcerned because of the apparent safety of the beach, even though the water was deep enough to drown him. He didn't understand his dependence upon his father. However, the farther they moved away from shore, the tighter the child held to his father. Like the child, we are always completely dependent upon the Lord to provide for us. However, often we don't recognize our dependence when we are "close to shore" experiencing the apparent security of financial prosperity. But when our possessions are few or none, it is easier to recognize our need and to cling to our heavenly Father.

Moreover, Hebrews 12:6, 10 tells us that, *"He scourges every son whom he receives . . . for our good that we may share His holiness."* If we have sin in our lives or a wrong attitude toward money, the Lord may discipline us by allowing financial difficulties to encourage us to forsake our sin.

If we have sin in our lives or a wrong attitude toward money, the Lord may discipline us by allowing financial difficulties to encourage us to forsake our sin.

4. The Mystery of God's Sovereignty

In Hebrews 11 we find "Faith's Hall of Fame." In verses 1-35 we have a list of people who triumphed miraculously by the exercise of their faith in God. But in verse 36 the writer directs our attention to godly people who gained God's approval, yet experienced poverty. God ultimately chooses how much to entrust to each person, and sometimes we simply can't understand His decisions.

LET'S SUMMARIZE: The Scriptures teach neither the necessity of poverty nor uninterrupted prosperity. What the Bible teaches is the responsibility of being a faithful steward. Please review this diagram which contrasts the three perspectives.

	Poverty	Stewardship	Prosperity
Possessions are:	Evil	A responsibility	A right
I work to:	Meet only basic needs	Serve Christ	Become rich
Godly people are:	Poor	Faithful	Wealthy
Ungodly people are:	Wealthy	Unfaithful	Poor
I give:	Because I must	Because I love God	To get
My spending is:	Without gratitude to God	Prayerful and responsible	Carefree and consumptive

Before we leave the issue of prosperity, it is important for us to understand the Lord's perspective of prosperity. The Lord evaluates true riches based on His spiritual value system, which is stated most clearly in Revelation. The godly poor are rich in God's sight. *"I [the Lord] know your tribulation and your poverty (but you are rich)"* (Revelation 2:9). Those who are wealthy, yet do not enjoy a close relationship with Christ are actually poor. *"Because you say, 'I am rich, and have become wealthy, and have need of nothing,' and you do not know that you are wretched and miserable and poor and blind and naked"* (Revelation 3:17). True prosperity extends far beyond material possessions. True prosperity is gauged by how well we know Jesus Christ and by how closely we follow Him.

WHY DO THE WICKED PROSPER?

This is a disturbing question God's people have asked for centuries. The prophet Jeremiah inquired of the Lord: *"You are always righteous, O Lord, when I bring a case before you. Yet I would speak with you about your justice: Why does the way of the wicked prosper?"* (Jeremiah 12:1, NIV).

Jeremiah

The Psalmist also asked why the wicked prospered, and he admitted being envious of them. Godliness did not seem to "pay off." Then the Lord revealed the wicked person's end—sudden eternal punishment. *"Surely God is good to . . . those who are pure in heart. But as for me, my feet had almost slipped . . . for I envied the arrogant when I saw the prosperity of the wicked . . .When I tried to understand all this, it was oppressive to me till I entered the sanctuary of God; then I understood their final destiny. Surely you place them on slippery ground; you cast them down to ruin. How suddenly are they destroyed, completely swept away by terrors!"* (Psalm 73:1-19, NIV).

The Bible tells us that some of the wicked will prosper, and not to envy them, because life on earth is short. *"Do not fret because of evil men or be envious of those who do wrong; for like the grass they will soon wither, like green plants they will soon die away"* (Psalm 37:1-2, NIV). We are to maintain the Lord's perspective and His eternal value system.

LITIGATION

More than 22,000 lawsuits are filed each day in our country—eight million per year! Unfortunately, many of these pit Christian against Christian. Suing seems to be a national pastime: A woman sued a man who she said kicked her at a nightclub. She sought $200,000 as compensation for the injury and lost time on the dance floor. A former professional football player was awarded $300,000 for the "psychological injury" suffered from being called a "chicken" by the team doctor.

There are a number of reasons for this flood of lawsuits, including an avalanche of new laws and most disturbing, that people are becoming less and less forgiving. The court system uses an adversarial judicial process, which frequently creates animosities and fractures relationships between the parties involved. Instead of trying to heal the wounds, the system provides a legal solution but leaves the problems of unforgiveness and anger untouched.

The Bible stresses that the goal should be reconciliation. *"If therefore you are presenting your offering at the altar, and there remember that your brother has something against you, leave your offering there before the altar, and go your way; first be reconciled to your brother"* (Matthew 5:23-24).

Scripture states that when Christians are at odds with one another, they should not settle their disputes through the courts. *"Does any one of you, when he has a case against his neighbor, dare to go to law before the unrighteous, and not before the saints? Or do you not know that the saints will judge the world? And if the world is judged by you, are you not competent to constitute the smallest law courts? Do you not know that we shall judge angels? How much more, matters of this life? If then you have law courts dealing with matters of this life, do you appoint them as judges who are of no account in the church? I say this to your shame. Is it so, that there is not among you one wise man who will be able to decide between his brethren, but brother goes to law with brother, and that before unbelievers? Actually, then, it is already a defeat for you, that you have lawsuits with one another. Why not rather be wronged? Why not rather be defrauded?"* (1 Corinthians 6:1-7).

Instead of initiating a lawsuit, a three-step procedure for Christians to resolve their differences is set forth in Matthew 18:15-17: *"And if your brother sins, go and reprove him in private; if he listens to you, you have won your brother. But if he does not listen to you, take one or two more with you, so that by the mouth of two or three witnesses every fact may be confirmed. And if he refuses to listen to them, tell it to the church; and if he refuses to listen even to the church, let him be to you as a Gentile and a tax-gatherer."*

Instead of initiating a lawsuit, a three-step procedure for Christians to resolve their differences is set forth in Matthew 18:15-17.

1. **Go in private.** The party who believes he has been wronged needs to confront the other person in private with his claims. If the dispute remains unresolved, then:
2. **Go with one or two others.** The person who feels wronged should return with witnesses who can confirm facts or help resolve the dispute. If this is still unsuccessful, then:
3. **Go before the church.** The third step is mediation or arbitration before an impartial group in the church or perhaps a conciliation service sponsored by a church or ministry if this is available in your area.

The greatest benefit of following this procedure is not simply reaching a fair settlement of the dispute, but practicing forgiveness and demonstrating love.

TAXES

What is the biblical perspective on paying taxes? That is the same question that was asked of Jesus. *"Is it lawful for us to pay taxes to Caesar or not? . . . [Jesus] said to them, 'Show Me a [Roman coin]. Whose likeness and inscription* does it have?' And they said, 'Caesar's.' And He said to them, 'Then give to Caesar the things that are to Caesars'" (Luke 20:22-25). This is an example of the contrast between the practices of our society and the teaching of Scripture. Avoid paying taxes at any cost, people rationalize; after all, the government squanders much of what it collects.

I am not condoning the waste found in government. In fact, I believe a citizen should make an effort to influence government to be more efficient. But the Bible tells us of an additional responsibility: to pay your taxes! *"Let every person be in subjection to the governing authorities. For there is no authority except from God, and those which exist are established by God . . . because of this you also pay taxes, for rulers are servants of God, devoting themselves to this very thing. Render to all what is due them: tax to whom tax is due"* (Romans 13:1, 6-7). It is permissible to reduce your taxes by using legal tax deductions, but we should be careful not to make unwise decisions simply to avoid paying taxes.

"Oh great, now I have to give unto Caesar, too."

PARTIALITY

Study carefully James 2:1-9, *"My brethren, do not hold your faith in our glorious Lord Jesus Christ with an attitude of personal favoritism. For if a man comes into your assembly with a gold ring and dressed in fine clothes, and there also comes in a poor man in dirty clothes, and you pay special attention to the one who is wearing the fine clothes . . . have you not made distinctions among yourselves, and become judges with evil motives? . . . If, however, you are fulfilling the royal law, according to the Scripture, 'You shall love your neighbor as yourself,' you are doing well. But if you show partiality, you are committing sin and are convicted by the law as transgressors."*

I have struggled with the sin of partiality, and this has unintentionally influenced my actions. Once, when I hung up the phone, my wife said, "I know you were not talking to Ken; it must have been Ryan. You like Ken better, and it shows in your voice."

Partiality does not have to be based on a person's wealth. It can also be based on a person's education, social position, or spiritual status. James 2:9 could not be more blunt: *"But if you show partiality, you are committing sin and are convicted by the law as transgressors."* How do we break the habit of partiality? Romans 12:10 tells us, *"Be devoted to one another in brotherly love; give preference to one another in honor."* And Philippians 2:3 reads, *"With humility of mind let each of you regard one another as more important than himself."* We need to ask the Lord to ingrain in our thinking the habit of consciously elevating each person regardless of his or her station in life, as more important than ourselves. One practical way to overcome partiality is to concentrate on the abilities of each person. Everyone can do some things better than I can. This realization helps me appreciate all people.

We need to ask the Lord to ingrain in our thinking the habit of consciously elevating each person regardless of his or her station in life, as more important than ourselves.

PERSPECTIVE NOTES

Moses—
Chose eternal rather than temporal values

"For what does it profit a man to gain the whole world,
and forfeit his soul?"
Mark 8:36

ETERNITY HOMEWORK

Scripture to Memorize:

"For what does it profit a man to gain the whole world, and forfeit his soul?" (Mark 8:36).

Practical Application: ☐ Complete the Determining Your Standard of Living practical application. ☐ Also complete and hand in to your leader the Evaluation and Suggestions sheet found in the back of the practical application workbook.

DAY ONE

Read the Perspective Notes on pages 155 to 165 and answer:

1. What was the most helpful concept you learned from the notes?

2. Do you sense the Lord would have you alter your lifestyle in any way? If so, in what way?

DAY TWO

Read *Psalm 39:4-6* and *Psalm 103:13-16* and answer:

1. What do these passages say to you about the length of life on earth?

Then read *Psalm 90:10, 12.*

2. Why do you think that Moses suggested numbering your days?

3. Estimate the number of days you have left on earth. How does this impact your thinking?

4. Based on your number of days what actions will you take?

5. In your own words contrast the brevity of life on earth with eternity.

DAY THREE

Read *1 Chronicles 29:15; Philippians 3:20;* **and** *1 Peter 2:11.*

1. What do these passages say about your identity on earth and in heaven?

   1 Chronicles 29:15—

   Philippians 3:20—

   1 Peter 2:11—

Then read *2 Peter 3:10-13.*

2. In the future what will happen to the earth?

3. How should this impact the way you invest your time and spend money?

DAY FOUR

Read *Ecclesiates 12:13-14* **and** *2 Corinthians 5:9-10.*

1. What will happen to each of us in the future?

   Ecclesiates 12:13-14—

   2 Corinthians 5:9-10—

Then read *1 Corinthians 3:11-15.*

2. How would you describe the works (give some examples) that will be burned at this final judgment?

3. Give some examples of works that will be rewarded.

4. Will all receive the same rewards in heaven?

5. What are you doing that will survive this final judgment?

DAY FIVE

Read *2 Corinthians 4:18.*

1. What does this verse say to you?

2. As you reflect on eternity, answer these questions thoughtfully: What three things do I want to accomplish during the rest of my life?

3. What do I wish to be remembered for?

4. What can I do during my lifetime that would contribute most significantly to the cause of Christ?

5. In light of these answers, what actions or changes do I need to make?

Read the Eternity notes and answer:

1. What was the most important concept you learned from reading the notes?

2. How will this impact you?

3. Please complete the Student Evaluation Sheet in the *Practical Application Workbook* to give to your leader. Describe what has been the most beneficial part of the Small Group Study for you:

 Please write your prayer requests in your prayer log before coming to class.

 I will take the following action as a result of this week's study:

ETERNITY NOTES 👑

Please do not read these notes until you completed the Eternity Homework.

On Monday, October 25, 1999 an unusual story was reported on the news. A private jet originating from Orlando, Florida was followed by Air Force jets that were unable to communicate with the pilots. Later I learned that two close friends of mine, Robert Fraley and Van Ardan, were on the airplane that carried golfer Payne Stewart to his death.

One of the most critical principles for us to understand is the reality of eternity. Robert and Van were men in their mid-forties. One of the most distinctive characteristics of them both was they lived their lives with a clear eternal perspective. Robert had framed these words in his workout area, "Take care of your body as though you will live forever; take care of your soul as if you will die tomorrow."

Because God loves us He reveals in the Scriptures that there is a heaven and hell, that there is a coming judgment, and that He will grant eternal rewards unequally. The Lord wants the best for us. Therefore, He wants to motivate us to invest our lives in such a way that we can enjoy an intimate relationship with Him now and receive the greatest possible eternal rewards and responsibilities in heaven.

Our failure to view our present lives through the lens of eternity is one of the biggest hindrances to seeing our lives and our assets in their true light. Yet Scripture states the reality of our eternal future should determine the character of our present life and the use of our money and possessions.

People who do not know the Lord look at life as a brief interval that begins at birth and ends at death. Looking to the future they see no further than their own life span. With no eternal perspective, they will think, *If this life is all there is, why deny myself any pleasure or possession?* Given this premise, why should they come to any other conclusion?

Those who know Christ are people of an entirely different perspective. We know life is short, it is the preface—not the book; the preliminaries—not the main event; the tune-up—not the concert. It is the testing period that will determine much of our experience in heaven.

Financial planners have a hard time convincing people to look down the road instead of simply focusing on today. "Don't think this year," they will tell you. "Think thirty years from now by planning." The wise person does indeed think ahead, but far more than thirty years—thirty million years ahead. As someone once said, "He who provides for this life but takes no care for eternity is wise for a moment but a fool forever." Jesus said it this way, *"For what does it profit a man to gain the whole world, and forfeit his soul?"* (Mark 8:36).

The reality of our eternal future should determine the character of our present life and the use of our money and possessions.

Throughout the Bible we are reminded that life on earth is brief—*"God is mindful that we are but dust"* (Psalm 103:14). Our earthly bodies are called *"tents"* (2 Peter 1:13, NIV), temporary dwelling places of our eternal souls. David recognized this and sought to gain God's perspective in light of the brevity of life. He asked of the Lord, *"Show me, O Lord, my life's end and the number of my days; let me know how fleeting is my life . . . Each person's life is but a breath. Man is a mere phantom as he goes to and fro: He bustles about, but only in vain; he heaps up wealth, not knowing who will get it"* (Psalm 39:4-6).

When a good friend discovered she had only a short time to live, she told me of her radical change in perspective. "The most striking thing that's happened," she said, "is that I find myself almost totally uninterested in accumulating more things. Things used to matter to me, but now I find my thoughts are centered on Christ, my friends, and other people."

Moses realized that true wisdom flowed out of understanding that our lives are short. So he asked the Lord to help him number the days he had on earth. *"As for the days of our life, they contain seventy years, or if due to strength, eighty years . . . for soon it is gone and we fly away . . . So teach us to number our days that we may present You a heart of wisdom"* (Psalm 90:10, 12). I encourage you to number the days you estimate that you have left on earth. If I live as long as my father, I have about 9,000 days left. This has helped me become aware that I need to invest my life and resources in eternally important matters.

When I served in the Navy, my attention was focused on the town in which I was stationed. However, as soon as I received orders discharging me in two months, I became what was called a "short-timer." My focus then completely shifted from the town I was going to leave, to my hometown. In a similar way, when I comprehend that I am really a "short-timer" on earth, and that soon I will be going to my real home, my focus will shift to things that will be important in heaven. In light of the brevity of life, Bible commentary author Matthew Henry said, "It ought to be the business of every day to prepare for our last day."

Eternity is Long

Eternity, on the other hand, *never ends*. It is forever. Imagine a cable running through the room where you are now. The cable runs out of the room to your right millions of light years all the way to the end of the universe and to your left to the other end of the universe. Now imagine that the cable to your left represents eternity past, and the cable to your right eternity future. You place a small mark on the cable in front of you. The mark represents your brief life on earth.

Because most people do not have an eternal perspective, they live as if the mark is all there is. They make mark choices. They live in mark houses, drive mark cars, wear mark clothes, live mark lifestyles, and raise mark children. Devotional writer A.W. Tozer referred to eternity as the "the long tomorrow." This is the backdrop against which all the questions of life and the handling of our resources must be understood and answered.

"Show me, O Lord, my life's end and the number of my days; let me know how fleeting is my life . . . Each person's life is but a breath. Man is a mere phantom as he goes to and fro: He bustles about, but only in vain; he heaps up wealth, not knowing who will get it."

PSALM 39:4-6, NIV

ETERNITY NOTES

Scripture tells us several things about our identity and role on this earth. First of all, *"Our citizenship is in heaven"* (Philippians 3:20), not earth. Secondly, *"We are ambassadors for Christ"* (2 Corinthians 5:20) representing Him on earth. Imagine an ambassador from a country who goes to work in another country that is generally hostile to his own. Naturally, he will want to learn about this new place, see the sights, and become familiar with the people and culture. But suppose eventually he becomes so much part of this foreign country that he begins to regard it as his true home. His allegiance wavers, and he gradually compromises his position as an ambassador, becoming increasingly ineffective in representing the best interests of his mother country.

We must never become too much at home in this world or we will become ineffective in serving the cause of the kingdom we are here to represent. We are aliens, strangers, and pilgrims on earth. Peter wrote, *"Since you will call on a Father who judges each man's work impartially, live your lives as strangers here in reverent fear"* (1 Peter 1:17, NIV). Later he added, *"I urge you, as aliens and strangers in the world, to abstain from sinful desires"* (1 Peter 2:11). Another Bible translation uses the words *"strangers and pilgrims"* (KJV).

The pilgrim is unattached. He is a traveler—not a settler—acutely aware that the excessive accumulation of things can distract him. Material things are valuable to the pilgrim, but only as they facilitate his or her mission. Things can entrench us in the present world. They can be like a chain around our legs making us unresponsive to God. If our eyes are focused on the visible, they will be drawn away from the invisible. *"So we fix our eyes not on what is seen, but on what is unseen. For what is seen is temporary, but what is unseen is eternal"* (2 Corinthians 4:18, NIV).

Pilgrims of faith look to the next world. They see earthly possessions for what they are—useful for kingdom purposes, but far too flimsy to bear the weight of trust, and wholly unable to survive the coming destruction of things. Thomas à Kempis, author of *The Imitation of Christ*, said it this way, "Let temporal things serve your use, but the eternal be the object of your desire." There are two principles concerning our possessions that will help us gain a proper perspective of them.

1. We Leave It All Behind

After John D. Rockefeller died his accountant was asked how much he left. The accountant's response was classic, "He left it all." Job said it this way, *"Naked I came from my mother's womb, and naked I shall return there"* (Job 1:21). Paul wrote, *"For we have brought nothing into the world, so we cannot take anything out of it either"* (1 Timothy 6:7).

The psalmist observed, *"Do not be afraid when a man becomes rich, when the glory of his house is increased; for when he dies he will carry nothing away; his glory will not descend after him. Though while he lives he congratulates himself—and though men praise you when you do well for yourself—he shall go to the generation of his fathers"* (Psalm 49:16-20).

"Let temporal things serve your use, but the eternal be the object of your desire."
—THOMAS À KEMPIS

2. Everything Will Be Destroyed

Earthly goods will not last forever—they are destined to be totally annihilated. *"But the day of the Lord will come like a thief. The heavens will disappear with a roar; the elements will be destroyed by fire, and the earth and everything in it will be laid bare. Since everything will be destroyed in this way, what kind of people ought you to be? You ought to live holy and godly lives"* (2 Peter 3:10-11, NIV). Understanding the temporary nature of possessions should influence us as we consider spending decisions.

JUDGMENT

It is uncomfortable to think about judgment. But the Bible unapologetically tells us that God will judge everyone according to our deeds: *"He has fixed a day in which He will judge the world in righteousness"* (Acts 17:31). All of us should live each day with this awesome awareness: *"But they will have to give an account to Him who is ready to judge the living and the dead"* (1 Peter 4:5, NIV).

God will judge us with total knowledge: *"Nothing in all creation is hidden from God's sight. Everything is uncovered and laid bare before the eyes of Him to whom we must give account"* (Hebrews 4:13, NIV). Because His knowledge is total, his judgment is comprehensive, *"Men will have to give account on the day of judgment for every careless word spoken"* (Matthew 12:36, NIV). His judgment extends to what is hidden from people. *"For God will bring every deed into judgment, including every hidden thing, whether it is good or evil"* (Ecclesiastes 12:14, NIV). He even *"will disclose the motives of each person's heart"* (1 Corinthians 4:5).

The Bible teaches all those who do not know Christ will be judged at the Great White Throne and sent to an indescribably dreadful place. *"And I saw a great white throne and Him who sat upon it . . . and I saw the dead, the great and the small standing before the throne . . . and they were judged, every one of them . . . If anyone's name was not found written in the book of life, he was thrown into the lake of fire"* (Revelation 20:11-15, NIV).

Judgment of Believers

After they die those who know Christ will spend eternity with the Lord in Heaven, an incredibly wonderful place. But what we seldom consider is that the entry point to heaven is a judgment.

Scripture teaches with unmistakable clarity that all believers in Christ will give an account of their lives to the Lord. *"For we shall all stand before the judgmentseat of God . . . so then each of us will give an account of himself to God"* (Romans 14:10-12). The result of this will be the gain or loss of eternal rewards. In 1 Corinthians 3:13-15 (NIV) it reads, *"His work will be shown for what it is, because the (Judgment) Day will bring it to light. If what he has built survives, he will receive his reward. If it is burned up, he will suffer loss."* Our works are what we have done with our time, influence, talents, and resources. God's Word does not treat this judgment as a meaningless formality before we get on to the real business of heavenly bliss. Rather, Scripture presents it as a monumental event in which things of eternal significance are brought to light.

> After they die those who know Christ will spend eternity with the Lord in Heaven, an incredibly wonderful place. But what we seldom consider is that the entry point to heaven is a judgment.

Why should I follow Scripture's guidance on money and possessions when it is so much fun to do whatever I please with my resources? I'm a Christian. I know I'm going to heaven anyway, so why get radical about the whole thing? Why not have the best of both worlds, this one and the next? Though few of us would be honest enough to use such language, these questions reflect a common attitude.

The prospect of eternal rewards for our obedience is a neglected key to unlocking our motivation. Paul was unashamedly motivated by the prospect of eternal rewards, and he acknowledged it frequently. Paul writes, *"I have fought the good fight, I have finished the course, I have kept the faith; in the future there is laid up for me the crown of righteousness, which the Lord, the righteous Judge, will award to me on that day"* (2 Timothy 4:7-8). He likewise encouraged all believers to be motivated by rewards. The Lord appeals not only to our compassion but also to our eternal self-interest. *"Love your enemies, and do good, and lend expecting nothing in return; and your reward will be great"* (Luke 6:35).

Our heavenly Father uses three things to motivate us to obey Him: the love of God, the fear of God, and the rewards of God. These are the same motivations that move my children to obey me. My children love me, and sometimes this is sufficient for them to be obedient. But other times it isn't enough. In a healthy sense, they also fear me. They know I will discipline them for wrongdoings. They also know I will reward them for doing right, with my words of approval, and sometimes in tangible ways.

John Wesley said, "I value all things only by the price they shall gain in eternity."

Unequal Rewards in Heaven

It is not so simple as saying, "I'll be in heaven and that's all that matters." On the contrary, Paul spoke about the loss of reward as a terrible loss. The receiving of rewards from Christ is an unspeakable gain. The loss of rewards from Christ is an unspeakable loss. Not all Christians will have the same rewards in heaven.

John Wesley said, "I value all things only by the price they shall gain in eternity." God's kingdom was the reference point for him. He committed to live as he did, not because he treasured no things, but because he treasured the right things. We often miss something in missionary martyr Jim Elliott's famous words, "He is no fool who gives what he cannot keep to gain what he cannot lose." We focus on his willingness to sacrifice, and so we should; however, we often overlook his motivation for gain. What separated him from many Christians was not that he did not want treasure, but that he wanted *real* treasure. Remember God loves you deeply. Because He wants the best for you throughout all eternity, God has revealed that today's sacrifices and service for Him will pay off forever.

IMPACTING ETERNITY TODAY

My use of my God-given resources of time, talents, and assets are the lever, positioned on the fulcrum of this life that moves the mountains of eternity.

Our daily choices will determine what will happen in the future. What we do in this life is of eternal importance. We only live on this earth once. *"It is appointed for men to die once and after this comes judgment"* (Hebrews 9:27). There is not such thing as reincarnation. Once our life on earth is over, you and I will never have another chance to move the hand of God through prayer, to share Christ with one who does not know the Savior, to give money to further God's kingdom, or to share with the poor and needy.

Those who dabble in photography understand the effect of the "fixer." In developing a photograph, the negatives are immersed in several different solutions. The developing solution parallels this life. As long as the photograph is in the developer solution it is subject to change. But when it is dropped in the fixer or "stop bath", it is permanently fixed. The photograph is now done. What you see is what you get. So it will be when we enter eternity — the lives we live on earth will be fixed as is, never to be altered or revised.

Alfred Nobel was a Swedish chemist who made his fortune by inventing dynamite and other powerful explosives, which were bought by governments to produce weapons. When Nobel's brother died one newspaper accidentally printed Alfred's obituary instead. He was described as a man who became rich by enabling people to kill each other with powerful weapons. Shaken from this assessment, Nobel resolved to use his fortune to reward accomplishments that benefited humanity, including what we now know as the Nobel Peace Prize. Let us put ourselves in Nobel's place. Let us read our own obituary, not as written by uninformed people, but as it would be written from heaven's point of view. Then let us use the rest of our lives to edit that obituary into what we really want it to be.

When I was a young boy I used to love playing Little League baseball. We played on a huge baseball field that had towering fences in the outfield. Years later, shortly after my father died, I spent the day walking around my old hometown reflecting on his life. When I visited the baseball field, I was shocked! It was so small. You could actually step over the outfield fences. While standing on pitcher's mound a thought struck me — many of those things that seem so large and important to us today shrink to insignificance in just a few years.

When I am face to face with Christ and look back on my life, I want to see that the things in which I invested my time, creativity, influence, and assets are big things to the Lord. I do not want to squander my life on those things that will not matter throughout eternity.

When Moses lived, Pharaoh was the most powerful person on earth. Pharaoh's daughter adopted Moses as an infant, and he had the opportunity to enjoy the wealth, power, and prestige of a member of the royal family. Hebrews 11:24-26 tells us what Moses later chose and why he decided it. *"By faith Moses, when he had grown up, refused to be called the son of Pharaoh's daughter; choosing rather to endure ill-treatment with the people of God, than to enjoy the passing pleasures of sin; considering the reproach of Christ greater riches than the treasures of Egypt; for he was looking to the reward."* Because Moses was looking forward to the only real rewards that would last, he chose to become a Hebrew slave and was used by God in a remarkable way.

What are the choices facing you now? How does an eternal perspective

My use of my God-given resources of time, talents, and assets are the lever, positioned on the fulcrum of this life that moves the mountains of eternity. Our daily choices will determine what will happen in the future.

influence your decisions? Martin Luther said that on his calendar there were only two days: "today" and "that Day." May we invest all that we are and have today in light of *that* day.

Author **Randy C. Alcorn** graciously contributed much of this chapter from his outstanding book *Money, Possessions and Eternity*. Used by permission of Tyndale House Publishers, Inc. All rights reserved.

LET'S REVIEW

At the beginning of this study we asked why the Bible said so much about money—in more than 2,350 verses. There are three major spiritual reasons: how we handle money impacts our fellowship with the Lord, money is the primary competitor with Christ for the lordship of our life, and money molds our character. Another reason is that the Lord wants us to have a blueprint for handling money so that we can become financially faithful in very practical ways.

Review this diagram of the wheel again. The eight areas of our responsibility, each with its primary thrust, are identified.

Faithfulness is a Journey
Applying the financial principles of Scripture is a journey that takes time. It's easy to become discouraged when your finances aren't completely under control by the end of this study. It takes the average person at least a year to apply most of these principles. Many Crown graduates decide to lead the study because they know the new students will help hold them accountable on this journey.

Faithfulness in Small Matters is Foundational
Many people also become frustrated by the inability to solve their financial problems quickly. Remember, simply be faithful with what you have—whether it is little or much. Some abandon the goal of becoming debt free or increasing their saving or giving, because the task looks impossible. And it may be without the Lord's help. Your job is to make a genuine effort, no matter how small it may appear, and then leave the results to God. I love what the Lord said to the prophet Zechariah, *"For who has despised the day of small things?"* (Zechariah 4:10). Don't be discouraged. Be diligent. Be persistent. Be faithful in even the smallest matters.

NOW IS THE TIME!

We are not economists. However, it is probable that our country will experience financially difficult times in the future. We don't know when this will occur or how it will manifest itself. We believe God has graciously given us a window of time to conform to His Word in the area of money. We plead with you to seize this opportunity! Become diligent in your efforts to get out of debt, give generously, budget persistently, and work as unto the Lord. In short, become a faithful steward.

You now know the biblical framework for managing money. But knowing is only half of the solution. You must act upon that knowledge. Jesus said, *"Every one who hears these words of Mine, and acts upon them, may be compared to a wise man, who built his house upon the rock. And the rain descended, and the floods came, and the winds blew, and burst against that house; and yet it did not fall; for it had been founded upon the rock. And every one who hears these words of Mine, and does not act upon them, will be like a foolish man, who built his house upon the sand. And the rain descended, and the floods came, and the winds blew, and burst against that house; and it fell, and great was its fall"* (Matthew 7:24-27).

The economic rain, floods and winds will someday burst against this country's financial house. If you have acted and built your house upon the solid principles found in Scripture, your house will not fall. One of the best ways to demonstrate your love for your family and friends is to get your financial house in order and encourage others to do the same.

If you have a desire to help others learn God's way of handling money, there are four places you can serve with Crown as illustrated in the baseball diamond below. First, you may serve as a small group leader or co-leader. They are the heroes of CROWN FINANCIAL MINISTRIES because the small group is where life-change takes place. Second base represents the opportunity to serve as the Church Coordinator or on the church team, if you want to impact your entire church. If you have a desire to influence your community, third base is for those who serve on the City Team. In order for Crown to have a broad impact on a larger city or populated area, it is necessary to have a full-time City Director and a functioning team of volunteers. Home plate is for those who have a "missionary spirit" and wish to help introduce Crown studies to other cities and even other countries.

Please tell your leader if you wish to become a leader or co-leader or if you wish to serve on the church team. If you want to serve your entire city or even beyond you city, contact CROWN FINANCIAL MINISTRIES at www.crown.org.

We appreciate the effort you have invested in this study. And we pray this has given you a greater appreciation for the Scriptures, helped you develop close friendships, and above all else, nurtured your love for Jesus Christ. May the Lord richly bless you.

PRAYER LOG
Be Faithful In Prayer

"Pray for one another . . . The effective prayer
of a righteous man can accomplish much."
James 5:16

"Pray for one another." — JAMES 5:16

Name _____   Spouse _____

Home phone _____   Children (ages) _____

Buisness phone _____   _____

E-mail _____   _____

Home address _____   _____

_____   _____

WEEK	PRAYER REQUEST(S)	ANSWERS TO PRAYER
1		
2		
3		
4		
5		
6		
7		
8		
9		
10		
11		
12	My long-term prayer request:	

PRAYER LOG

"Pray for one another." — JAMES 5:16

Name _____   Spouse _____

Home phone _____   Children (ages) _____

Buisness phone _____   _____

E-mail _____   _____

Home address _____   _____

_____   _____

WEEK	PRAYER REQUEST(S)	ANSWERS TO PRAYER
1		
2		
3		
4		
5		
6		
7		
8		
9		
10		
11		
12	My long-term prayer request:	

"Pray for one another." — JAMES 5:16

Name _____   Spouse _____

Home phone _____   Children (ages) _____

Buisness phone _____   _____

E-mail _____   _____

Home address _____   _____

_____   _____

WEEK	PRAYER REQUEST(S)	ANSWERS TO PRAYER
1		
2		
3		
4		
5		
6		
7		
8		
9		
10		
11		
12	My long-term prayer request:	

PRAYER LOG

"Pray for one another." — JAMES 5:16

Name _____   Spouse _____

Home phone _____   Children (ages) _____

Buisness phone _____   _____

E-mail _____   _____

Home address _____   _____

_____   _____

WEEK	PRAYER REQUEST(S)	ANSWERS TO PRAYER
1		
2		
3		
4		
5		
6		
7		
8		
9		
10		
11		
12	My long-term prayer request:	

PRAYER LOG

"Pray for one another." — JAMES 5:16

Name _____   Spouse _____

Home phone _____   Children (ages) _____

Buisness phone _____   _____

E-mail _____

Home address _____   _____

_____   _____

WEEK	PRAYER REQUEST(S)	ANSWERS TO PRAYER
1		
2		
3		
4		
5		
6		
7		
8		
9		
10		
11		
12	My long-term prayer request:	

PRAYER LOG

"Pray for one another." — JAMES 5:16

Name _____   Spouse _____
Home phone _____   Children (ages) _____
Buisness phone _____   _____
E-mail _____   _____
Home address _____   _____
_____   _____

WEEK	PRAYER REQUEST(S)	ANSWERS TO PRAYER
1		
2		
3		
4		
5		
6		
7		
8		
9		
10		
11		
12	My long-term prayer request:	

"Pray for one another." — JAMES 5:16

Name _____ Spouse _____

Home phone _____ Children (ages) _____

Buisness phone _____ _____

E-mail _____ _____

Home address _____ _____

_____ _____

WEEK	PRAYER REQUEST(S)	ANSWERS TO PRAYER
1		
2		
3		
4		
5		
6		
7		
8		
9		
10		
11		
12	My long-term prayer request:	

"Pray for one another." — JAMES 5:16

Name _____   Spouse _____

Home phone _____   Children (ages) _____

Buisness phone _____   _____

E-mail _____   _____

Home address _____   _____

_____   _____

WEEK	PRAYER REQUEST(S)	ANSWERS TO PRAYER
1		
2		
3		
4		
5		
6		
7		
8		
9		
10		
11		
12	My long-term prayer request:	

"Pray for one another." — JAMES 5:16

Name _____   Spouse _____

Home phone _____   Children (ages) _____

Buisness phone _____   _____

E-mail _____   _____

Home address _____   _____

_____   _____

WEEK	PRAYER REQUEST(S)	ANSWERS TO PRAYER
1		
2		
3		
4		
5		
6		
7		
8		
9		
10		
11		
12	My long-term prayer request:	

PRAYER LOG